Poisson and Other Distributions in Traffic

ENO FOUNDATION FOR TRANSPORTATION
SAUGATUCK   · 1971 ·   CONNECTICUT

Eno Foundation for Transportation

Saugatuck, Connecticut 06880

Poisson and Other Distributions in Traffic

The Poisson and Other Probability Distributions in Highway Traffic

DANIEL L. GERLOUGH

Professor of Transportation Engineering
University of Minnesota

FRANK C. BARNES

Transportation Planner
Southern California Rapid Transit District

Probability Theory Applied to Vehicle Distribution on Two-Lane Highways

ANDRÉ SCHUHL

Ingenieur General des Ponts et Chaussees
Marseille, France

ENO FOUNDATION FOR TRANSPORTATION

SAUGATUCK · 1971 · CONNECTICUT

MATH-STAT.

FOREWORD

In 1955 the Eno Foundation published *Poisson and Traffic,*
which dealt with the applications of the Poisson distribution
(and the negative exponential distribution) to the problems of
street and highway traffic. Techniques were given for fitting
the Poisson distribution to traffic data, for testing goodness of
fit, and for interpretation of the results.

During the intervening years there has been extensive research into various distributions suitable for traffic data. Distributions have now been grouped in two general classes: counting
distributions and interval distributions. Counting distributions
are useful for description of phenomena which are *discrete*
(i.e., have only integer values) such as the number of cars
counted during an interval of time, the number of parking
spaces available at a given instant, etc. Interval distributions
are useful for describing phenomena which are characterized
by measuring the interval between events such as the time between arrivals of vehicles at a given point, the distance between
vehicles at a given instant, and so on; such measurements
are *continuous* in that fractional values are permitted.

In publishing this revised monograph it is the aim of the
Eno Foundation to extend the range of applications described
in *Poisson and Traffic.* While some of the examples of that
work have been retained, many new ones have been added.
Counting distributions other than the Poisson are described, as
are interval distributions other than the negative exponential.
The objective has been not to develop new theories nor to
prove interesting theorems, but rather to present previously
developed theories in a form that will make them useful to
the practicing traffic engineer.

TABLE OF CONTENTS

FIGURES

LIST OF TABLES

The Poisson and Other Probability Distributions in Highway Traffic

DANIEL L. GERLOUGH

FRANK C. BARNES

Chapter I

INTRODUCTION

Traditionally, engineers have used formulas or "laws" to describe the behavior of physical systems. Although all physical systems have randomness in their behavior, most engineering analysis treats systems as though they were deterministic (nonrandom). This practice can be very acceptable where the particles are very small and the populations of particles are very large, such as when dealing with gases or electric currents. When, however, the populations become relatively small and the particles relatively large so that the observer finds himself measuring the behavior of individual particles, attention to random properties becomes all-important. Such is the situation with automobile traffic.

This monograph deals with some of the relationships which have been found useful in handling the random properties of traffic. One principal tool is the Poisson distribution, named after Simeon Denis Poisson, a French mathematician who carried out many of the early studies on probability. As will be seen, however, the Poisson distribution has certain limitations in its application, and other distributions may provide greater accuracy in certain cases.

NATURE OF THE POISSON DISTRIBUTION

When events of a given group occur in discrete degrees (heads or tails, 1 to 6 on the face of a die, etc.) the possibility of occurrence of a particular event in a specified number of trials may be described by the Bernoulli or binomial distribution (See Appendices B and C).

As an example, let us consider an experiment consisting of

five successive drawings of a ball from an urn containing uniformly mixed black and white balls, with the drawn ball being returned to the urn after each drawing. Of the five drawings which comprise a single experiment, let x be the number which produced black balls, i.e., the number of black balls in a sample of 5 where each drawing had a uniform probability. Thus x can equal 0, 1, 2, 3, 4, or 5. Let P(x) be the probability that in a given experiment the number of black balls would be exactly x. If p is the probability that a particular drawing will yield a black ball, and q ($q = 1 - p$) is the probability that a particular drawing yields a white ball, then

$$P(x) = C_x^5 p^x q^{5-x}$$

where C_x^5 is the number of combinations of 5 things taken x at a time. It can be seen that in the above example p, the probability that a single drawing yields a black ball, is equal to the percentage (written as a decimal fraction) of black balls in the urn. With the ball being replaced after each drawing p will remain constant from drawing to drawing.

The experiment just described is an example of the "Bernoulli" or "binomial" distribution in which P(x), the probability of exactly x successes out of n trials of an event where the probability of success remains constant from event to event, is given by

$$P(x) = C_x^n p^x q^{n-x}$$

If the number of items in the sample n, becomes very large while the product $pn = m$ is a finite constant, the binomial distribution approaches the Poisson distribution as a limit. This implies that the probability of occurrence, p, becomes very small.

$$\lim_{n \to \infty} P(x) = \frac{m^x e^{-m}}{x!}$$
$$pn = m$$

where e is the Napierian base of logarithms. ($e = 2.71828 \ldots$)

The derivation of the Poisson distribution as a limiting case of the binomial distribution is given in Appendix D. (The Poisson distribution can be derived independently of the binomial distribution by more advanced concepts. See Appendix D or Fry (*1*).

The mathematical conditions of an infinite number of trials and an infinitesimal probability are never achieved in practical problems. Nevertheless, the Poisson distribution is useful as approximating the binomial distribution under appropriate conditions.*

For such practical purposes, then, the Poisson distribution may be stated as follows:

If in a given experiment the number of opportunities for an event to occur is large (e.g., $n \geqslant 50$)

and

If the probability that a particular event occurs is small (e.g., $p \leqslant 0.1$)

and

If the average number of times the event occurs has a finite value, m ($m = np$)

$$\text{Then} \quad P(x) = \frac{m^x e^{-m}}{x!}$$

where $x = 0, 1, 2, \ldots$

In this statement of the Poisson distribution an experiment may consist of such things as:

a. Observing the number of micro-organisms in a standard sample of blood, x representing the number of micro-organisms in any one sample.

b. Observing the number of alpha particles emitted during each successive interval of t seconds. The number of such intervals will be j, and $x_1, x_2 \ldots x_j$ will be the number of particles during the 1st, 2nd, . . . jth intervals.

* It may also be noted that under appropriate conditions the binomial distribution may be approximated by the normal distribution.

c. Observing the number of blowholes in each of k castings, x representing the number of holes in any one casting.

d. Observing the number of cars passing a given point during each 30-second period, i representing the number of periods observed and x representing the number of cars in any 30-second period.

HISTORICAL BACKGROUND OF POISSON DISTRIBUTION

The first record of the use of the Poisson distribution to treat populations having the properties described is attributed to Bortkiewicz who studied the frequency of death due to the "kick of a horse" among the members of ten Prussian cavalry corps during a period of 20 years (2). A summary of his study is shown in Example 1, which compares actual and computed frequencies.

Example 1

THE NUMBER OF MEN IN TEN PRUSSIAN CAVALRY CORPS KILLED BY A HORSE KICK IN THE TWENTY YEARS 1875–1894

Number of deaths per corps-year	Observed number of corps-years during which the given number of deaths occurred.	Theoretical number of corps-years during which the given number of deaths occurred (as computed from the Poisson distribution)
0	109	108.7
1	65	66.3
2	22	20.2
3	3	4.1
4	1	0.6
5 and over	0	0.1

Some of the earliest engineering problems treated by the Poisson distribution were telephone switching problems. The following example is based on such data (3):

Example 2

CONNECTIONS TO WRONG NUMBER

Number of wrong connections per period	Observed number of periods during which the given number of wrong connections occurred	Theoretical number of periods exhibiting the given number of wrong connections (Poisson distribution)
0	0	0.0
1	0	0.3
2	1	1.6
3	5	4.8
4	11	10.4
5	14	18.2
6	22	26.4
7	43	33.1
8	31	36.0
9	40	35.2
10	35	30.7
11	20	24.3
12	18	17.9
13	12	12.0
14	7	7.5
15	6	4.3
16	2	2.4
>16	0	1.9

Following the pioneer work in the field of telephone applications, the Poisson distribution was gradually applied to other engineering problems. The following example adapted from Grant (4) shows an application to the occurrence of excessive rainfall:

Example 3

RAINSTORMS

Number of storms per station per year	Observed number of occurrences	Theoretical number of occurrences (Poisson distribution)
0	102	99.3
1	114	119.1
2	74	71.6
3	28	28.7
4	10	8.6
5	2	2.0
>5	0	0.7
Total	330	330.0

The application of the Poisson distribution to traffic problems is not new. Certain applications were discussed by Kinzer (5) in 1933, Adams (6) in 1936, and Greenshields (7) in 1947.

The first published examples were those of Adams. The following is one of his examples:

Example 4

RATE OF ARRIVAL (Vere St.)

(Number of vehicles arriving per 10 second interval)

Number of vehicles per 10 second period	Observed frequency	Total vehicles	Theoretical frequency
0	94	0	97.0
1	63	63	59.9
2	21	42	18.5
3	2	6	3.8
>3	0	0	0.8
Total	180	111	180.0

Note: Since there were 111 vehicles in 180 ten-second periods, the hourly volume was 222.

REFERENCES FOR CHAPTER I

1. Fry, Thornton C., *Probability and Its Engineering Uses*, Van Nostrand, 1965, pp. 240–243.
2. Bortkiewicz, Ladislaus von, *Das Gesetz der kleinen Zahlen*, B.G. Teubner, Leipzig, 1898.
3. Thorndike, Frances, "Application of Poisson's Probability Summation," *Bell System Technical Journal*, vol. 5, no. 4, October 1926, pp. 604–624.
4. Grant, Eugene L., "Rainfall Intensities and Frequencies," *Transactions*, American Society of Civil Engineers, vol. 103, 1938, pp. 384–388.
5. Kinzer, John P., *Application of the Theory of Probability to Problems of Highway Traffic*, thesis submitted in partial satisfaction of requirements for degree of B.C.E., Polytechnic Institute of Brooklyn, June 1, 1933.
   Abstracted in: *Proceedings*, Institute of Traffic Engineers, vol. 5, 1934, pp. 118–124.
6. Adams, William F., "Road Traffic Considered as a Random Series," *Journal*, Institution of Civil Engineers, vol. 4, Nov., 1936, pp. 121–130.
7. Greenshields, Bruce D., Schapiro, Donald, and Ericksen, Elroy L., *Traffic Performance at Urban Street Intersections*, Technical Report No. 1, Yale Bureau of Highway Traffic, 1947.

Chapter II

SELECTING AND FITTING COUNTING DISTRIBUTIONS TO DATA

Engineers use probability distributions in two ways: analysis of data on observed behavior, and prediction of future behavior. Data analysis is aided by fitting a distribution to the data. When experience has shown the type of distribution that is applicable to a particular physical phenomenon, then that distribution can be used to predict the frequencies of various future conditions. Thus, a discussion of distributions appropriately starts with a description of fitting procedures.

FITTING DISTRIBUTION TO DATA

The most easily used method of fitting a distribution to data is known as the *method of moments*. This title arises from the fact that one computes the sample moments (arithmetic mean, variance, etc.) and thereby estimates the moments or parameters of the desired distribution.

Another fitting technique is the *method of maximum likelihood (1)*. In certain situations this technique provides for greater accuracy, but is more difficult and time consuming to use. The method of moments is particularly straightforward in fitting the Poisson distribution.

Poisson Distribution and Method of Moments

As an example, consider the experimental data on wrong connections previously mentioned. Fitting of the Poisson distribution to the data (by the method of moments) can be carried out in tabular form, as follows:

Example 5

CONNECTIONS TO WRONG NUMBER

Col. 1 x = Number of wrong connections (per period)	Col. 2 f = Observed frequency (periods)	Col. 3 fx = Total wrong connections	Col. 4 P(x) = Theoretical probability (Poisson)	Col. 5 P(x) · Σf = F(x) Theoretical frequency (periods)
0	0	0	0.000	0.0
1	0	0	0.001	0.3
2	1	2	0.006	1.6
3	5	15	0.018	4.8
4	11	44	0.039	10.4
5	14	70	0.068	18.2
6	22	132	0.099	26.4
7	43	301	0.124	33.1
8	31	248	0.135	36.0
9	40	360	0.132	35.2
10	35	350	0.115	30.7
11	20	220	0.091	24.3
12	18	216	0.067	17.9
13	12	156	0.045	12.0
14	7	98	0.028	7.5
15	6	90	0.016	4.3
16	2	32	0.009	2.4
>16	0	0	0.007	1.9
Total	267	2334	1.000	267.0

Columns 1 and 2 contain the observed data.

The entries in Col. 3 are the products of the corresponding entries in Col. 1 and Col. 2.

m = average number of wrong connections per period

$$= \frac{\text{total number of wrong connections}}{\text{total number of periods}} = \frac{2334}{267} = 8.742$$

Then, according to the definition of the Poisson distribution,

$$P(x) = \frac{m^x e^{-m}}{x!} = \frac{(8.742)^x e^{-8.742}}{x!}$$

Methods of evaluating e^{-x}, x!, and P(x) are discussed in the appendices. For the present it is sufficient to state that

$$e^{-8.742} = 0.15973 \times 10^{-4}$$

The value of P(x) corresponding to each value of x is calculated, using the formula above, and tabulated in Column 4. The calculated or theoretical frequency (Column 5) is obtained:

$$\begin{aligned} \text{Calculated (Theoretical) Frequency} &= \text{(Total periods observed) P(x)} \\ &= 267 \text{ P(x)} \end{aligned}$$

Note: When theoretical frequencies (Column 5) are calculated, fractional (decimal) values often result. Here these values have been rounded-off to the nearest 0.1. The observed frequencies will, of course, always be integral numbers. In the last row of the table (for more than 16 wrong connections per period) the values of probability and theoretical frequency are necessary to make the totals balance. These values represent the summation from 17 to infinity.

It is seen that there is a high degree of agreement between the observed and calculated frequencies in this example.

Fitting Traffic Data

Example 6 demonstrates the fitting of a Poisson distribution to traffic arrival data.

Testing Goodness of Fit (χ^2 Test)

In each of the foregoing examples it has been postulated that a Poisson distribution having a parameter m whose value has been computed from the observed data describes the population that has been sampled. The observed distribution constitutes this sample. By inspection there is apparent agreement between the observed distribution (sample) and the theoretical distribution. The inference is then made that the postulated theoretical (Poisson) distribution is in fact the true population distribution. This inference is based, however, solely on in-

Example 6

TRAFFIC ARRIVALS: 30-SECOND INTERVALS
(Durfee Avenue, Northbound)

Number of cars per interval x_i	Observed frequency* f_i	Total cars observed $f_i x_i$	Probability of x_i $P(x_i)$	Theoretical frequency F_i
0	9	0	0.047	5.6
1	16	16	0.143	17.2
2	30	60	0.219	26.3
3	22	66	0.224	26.9
4	19	76	0.172	20.6
5	10	50	0.105	12.6
6	3	18	0.054	6.5
7	7	49	0.023	2.8
8	3	24	0.009	1.1
$\geqslant 9$	1	9	0.002	0.4
Total	120	368	1.000	120.0

$$m = \frac{368}{120} = 3.067 \quad e^{-m} = 0.047$$

$$F_i = 120 \, P(x_i)$$

* Data by courtesy of Los Angeles County Road Department.

spection; a more rigorous basis for reaching such a conclusion is desired. One of several statistical tests of significance may be used for this purpose; the chi square (χ^2) test is appropriate to the present application. This test, which is described in Appendix G and illustrated below, provides for one of two decisions:

1. It is not very likely that the true distribution (of which the observed data constitute a sample) is in fact identical with the postulated distribution.
2. The true distribution (of which the observed data constitute a sample) could be identical with the postulated distribution.

It can be seen that either decision can be erroneously made.

Decision 1 can be wrong if in fact the postulated distribution is the true distribution. On the other hand, Decision 2 can be wrong if the true distribution is in fact different from the postulated distribution. Statistical tests of significance allow for specifying the probability (or risk) of making either of these types of error. Usually the probability of making the first type of error (incorrectly rejecting the postulated distribution when in fact it is identical with the true distribution) is specified and no statement is made with regard to the second type of error. The specification of the first type of error is expressed as a "significance level." Common significance levels are 0.01, 0.05, and 0.10. Thus, when a test is made at the 0.05 (5%) level, the engineer takes the chance (risk) that 5% of the rejected postulated distributions are in fact identical with the corresponding true distributions. For a complete discussion of the theory underlying this and other statistical tests of significance, the reader is referred to any standard text on statistics.

The technique of performing the χ^2 significance test is illustrated in Example 7. In the table of Example 7 the observed frequency of wrong connections is shown along with the postulated theoretical frequency distribution (computed in Example 5). The problem is to decide whether the observed data can be construed as a sample coming from the postulated theoretical distribution. The computing technique described in Appendix G yields a chi square value of 7.6 with 11 degrees of freedom. (It should be noted in the table of Example 7 that the frequencies of 3 or fewer wrong connections have been combined, as have the frequencies of 15 or more. This is done to meet the requirement of the χ^2 test that the *theoretical frequency be at least 5 in any group.* Thus, this combination results in 13 groups, with $v = 13 - 2 = 11$ degrees of freedom.)

From statistical tables or from Figure G1 (in Appendix G) the value of χ^2 at the 0.05 (5%) significance level for $v = 11$ is found to be 19.7.* This is known as the critical value for

---

* In using tables of χ^2 care should be exercised to note the manner in which the table is entered with the significance level. If the table is so constructed that for a given number of degrees of freedom the value of χ^2 increases with *decreasing* percentiles (probabilities), the table is entered with the percentile correspond-

Example 7

χ^2 TEST OF CONNECTIONS TO WRONG NUMBER
(Data from Example 2)

Number of wrong connections per period x	Observed frequency f	Postulated (theoretical) frequency F	f^2/F
3	6	6.7	5.4
4	11	10.4	11.6
5	14	18.2	10.8
6	22	26.4	18.3
7	43	33.1	55.9
8	31	36.0	26.7
9	40	35.2	45.5
10	35	30.7	39.9
11	35	24.3	16.5
12	18	17.9	18.1
13	12	12.0	12.0
14	7	7.5	6.5
⩾15	8	8.6	7.4
Total	267	267.0	274.6

$$\chi^2 = 274.6 - 267.0 = 7.6$$

the significance test at the 5% level. Since the computed value of χ^2 (7.6) is less than the critical value, decision 2 is accepted. (The acceptance of decision 2 is rigorously stated, "There is no evidence to indicate that the true distribution differs from the postulated distribution.") Had the computed value of χ^2 exceeded the critical value, decision 1 would have been accepted.

Once the decision has been made that a particular postulated theoretical distribution appropriately represents the population from which the observed data came, the theoretical distribution can be used in place of the observed distribution for engineering analysis and action, since it will be free from the random variations present in the observed distribution.

ing to the significance level. If the table is such that the value of χ^2 increases with *increasing* percentiles, the table is entered with the significance level subtracted from one. (In this case $1.00 - .05 = 0.95$).

Other Applications

Certain analyses of parking may be treated by the Poisson distribution. Example 8 shows the results of a study of 4 block faces containing 48 one-hour parking spaces. (Loading zones and short-time parking spaces were not included.) Observations were taken during the hours of 2 P.M. to 4 P.M. on the days Monday through Friday. The observation period was divided into 5-minute intervals. During each 5-minute interval one observation was made; the exact time of observation within each interval was randomized. Each observation consisted of an instantaneous count of the number of vacant spaces. Since the χ^2 test shows good agreement between the observed and theoretical data, there is no ground to doubt that the distribution of vacant parking spaces follows the Poisson distribution. Assuming the Poisson distribution to hold, it is possible to compute the probability of finding a vacant one-hour parking space within these four block faces.

Example 8

VACANT PARKING SPACES
(Westwood Blvd.)

Number of vacant 1-hour parking spaces per observation	Observed frequency f	Theoretical frequency F	f^2/F
0	29	25.1	33.5
1	42	39.3	44.9
2	21	30.1	14.7
3	16	16.4	15.6
4	7 ⎤	6.4 ⎤	
5	2 ⎥ 12	2.0 ⎥ 9.1	15.8
6	3 ⎥	0.5 ⎥	
⩾7	0 ⎦	0.2 ⎦	
	120	120.0	124.5

(The brackets indicate grouping for the χ^2 test.)

$$m = \frac{188}{120} = 1.567 \qquad e^{-m} = 0.209 \qquad s^2 = 2.063$$

$$\sum \frac{f^2}{F} - n = 124.5 - 120.0 = 4.5 \qquad\qquad s^2/m = 1.317$$

$$\upsilon = 5 - 2 = 3$$

$$\chi^2_{.05} = 7.81$$

The probability of finding one or more vacant parking spaces, $P(\geqslant 1)$, is

$$P(\geqslant 1) = 1 - P(0) = 1 - e^{-m} = 1 - 0.209 = 0.791$$

NON-POISSON TRAFFIC DATA

Some Examples

Not all traffic data follow the Poisson distribution. Example 9 is an analysis of right turns during 300 three-minute intervals distributed throughout various hours of the day and various days of the week. While casual inspection of the observed data might lead one to suspect randomness, the test shows strong evidence of non-Poisson behavior which is interpreted as non-randomness.

Example 9

RIGHT TURNS

(Westwood at Pico)

Number of cars making right turns per 3-minute interval	Observed frequency f	Theoretical frequency F	f^2/F
0	14	6.1	32.1
1	30	23.7	38.0
2	36	46.2	28.1
3	68	59.9	77.2
4	43	58.3	31.7
5	43	45.4	40.7
6	30	29.4	30.6
7	14	16.4	12.0
8	10	8.0	12.5
9	6 ⎤	3.4 ⎤	
10	4 ⎟	1.3 ⎟	
11	1 ⎬ 12	0.6 ⎬ 6.6	21.8
12	1 ⎟	0.3 ⎟	
⩾13	0 ⎦	1.0 ⎦	
	300	300.0	324.7

(The brackets indicate grouping for the χ^2 test.)

$$m = \frac{1168}{300} = 3.893 \qquad e^{-m} = 0.0203 \qquad s^2 = 5.213$$

$$\sum \frac{f^2}{F} - n = 324.7 - 300.0 = 24.7 \qquad\qquad s^2/m = 1.339$$

$$v = 10 - 2 = 8$$

$$\chi^2_{.05} = 15.5$$

Since $24.7 > 15.5$, the fit is *not* acceptable at the 5% significance level.

Example 10 is another instance where a χ^2 test fails and the data may be presumed not to follow the Poisson distribution. This may be related to local conditions at the observation site, such as the effect of traffic signals. In situations where the χ^2 test fails for the Poisson distribution, the engineer may wish to investigate some other distribution. See Example 13.

Example 10

ARRIVAL RATE—10-SECOND INTERVALS
(Durfee Avenue, Northbound)

Number of cars per interval	Observed frequency* f	Theoretical frequency F	f²/F
0	139	129.6	149.1
1	128	132.4	123.7
2	55	67.7	44.7
3	25	23.1	27.1
4	10 ⎫	5.9 ⎫	
5	3 ⎬ 13	1.2 ⎬ 7.2	23.5
≥6	0 ⎭	0.1 ⎭	
	360	360.0	368.1

(As before, the brackets indicate grouping for the χ^2 test)

$$m = \frac{368}{360} = 1.022 \qquad e^{-m} = 0.360$$

$$\sum \frac{f^2}{F} - n = 368.1 - 360.0 = 8.1 \qquad s^2 = 1.203$$

$$\upsilon = 5 - 2 = 3 \qquad s^2/m = 1.177$$

$$\chi^2_{.05} = 7.81$$

* Data by courtesy of Los Angeles County Road Department.

The fit is, therefore, *not* acceptable at the 5% level.

The raw data utilized in Example 10 were also analyzed in 30 second intervals. This analysis is shown in Example 11.

Example 11

ARRIVAL RATE—30-SECOND INTERVALS
(Durfee Avenue, Northbound)

Number of cars per interval	Observed frequency f	Theoretical frequency F	f^2/F
0	9	5.6	14.5
1	16	17.2	14.9
2	30	26.3	34.2
3	22	26.9	18.0
4	19	20.6	17.5
5	10	12.6	7.9
6	3 ⎫	6.5 ⎫	
7	7 ⎬ 14	2.8 ⎬ 10.8	18.1
8	3 ⎪	1.1 ⎪	
≥9	1 ⎭	0.4 ⎭	
	120	120.0	125.1

$$m = \frac{368}{120} - 3.067 \qquad e^{-m} = 0.047$$

$$\sum \frac{f^2}{F} - n = 125.1 - 120.0 = 5.1$$

$$v = 7 - 2 = 5$$

$$\chi^2_{.05} = 11.1$$

This fit *is* acceptable at the 5% significance level.

The fact that a Poisson distribution fits data analyzed in 30-second intervals but not the same data analyzed in 10-second intervals may indicate some local effect that produces non-random effects (for example, a traffic signal which causes bunching or cyclic effects during certain portions of the signal cycle).

It is interesting to note that when two or more Poisson populations are mixed, the result is a Poisson population. See Appendix I.

Data With Unusually High Variability

As discussed in Appendix F, one important characteristic of the Poisson distribution is that the mean and variance are equal. Thus, when the ratio of the variance to the mean of experimental data is approximately 1, the Poisson distribution will fit the data well. When, however, the ratio of the variance to the mean is substantially greater than 1, as may be the case where the mean value varies during the course of the measurements, or where the period of observations is short by comparison to some cyclic phenomenon, the Poisson distribution may not fit acceptably. In such cases, where the variance is substantially greater than the mean, the negative-binomial distribution may produce an acceptable fit.

The Negative-Binomial Distribution

The negative-binomial distribution which is sometimes called the Pascal distribution may be stated by the following expression:

$$P(x) = C_{k-1}^{x+k-1} p^k q^x$$

if $\qquad$ $m = $ mean of observed data

$\qquad$ $s^2 = $ variance of observed data

then $\qquad$ $p = m/s^2$

$$k = \frac{m^2}{s^2 - m} \left.\right\} \text{(see Ref. 2, page 12)}$$

$$q = (1 - p)$$

Example 12 shows the results of fitting a negative-binomial distribution to the data of Example 10. The chi-square test indicates a very acceptable fit, whereas the fit of the Poisson distribution (in Example 10) was not acceptable. Fitting is accomplished by using the sample mean and sample variance to estimate p and k. The various terms can then be obtained from tables (2), or by direct computation (e.g., using a computer program).

Example 12

NEGATIVE BINOMIAL DISTRIBUTION FIT TO DATA OF EXAMPLE 10
ARRIVAL RATE—10-SECOND INTERVALS
(Durfee Avenue, Northbound)

Number of cars per interval x_i	Observed frequency f_i	Probability $P(x_i)^*$	Theoretical frequency F_i	f_i^2/F_i
0	139	0.3939	141.8	136.3
1	128	0.3376	121.5	134.8
2	55	0.1709	61.5	49.2
3	25	0.0666	24.0	26.0
4	10 ⎫	0.0221	8.0 ⎫	
5	3 ⎬ 13	0.0066	2.4 ⎬ 11.2	15.1
>5	0 ⎭	0.0021	0.8 ⎭	
	360	1.0000	360.0	362.4

$$\chi^2 = 362.4 - 360.0 = 2.4 \qquad m = 1.022$$

$$v = 5 - 3 = 2 \qquad s^2 = 1.203$$

$$\chi^2_{05,2} = 5.99 \qquad s^2/m = 1.177$$

* The probability values were obtained by a two-way interpolation of William-son and Bretherton's tables to obtain a table for $p = 0.85$ and $k = 5.75$. When a computer program was used for fitting, the results were

x_i	F_i
0	140.4
1	122.0
2	62.2
3	24.2
4	8.0
5	2.3
6	0.9

These values produce a slightly better χ^2 value.

Thus the fit is acceptable at the 5% level.

Data With Unusually Low Variability

When the presence of one car influences the behavior of cars behind it, such as in heavy traffic, the ratio of the variance to the mean of observed data may be less than 1. When this ratio is substantially less than 1, the Poisson distribution usually will not produce an acceptable fit, but other distributions may do so. Useful distributions for such cases include the generalized-Poisson distribution and the binomial distribution.

Generalized-Poisson Distribution

Each term of the generalized-Poisson distribution consists of the sum of k terms of the simple Poisson distribution. This may be stated

$$P(x) = \sum_{j=kx}^{k(x+1)-1} \frac{\lambda^j e^{-\lambda}}{j!}$$

or

$$P(x) = \sum_{i=1}^{k} \frac{e^{-\lambda} (\lambda)^{xk+i-1}}{(xk + i - 1)!}$$

That is,

for k = 2

$$P(0) = e^{-\lambda} + \lambda e^{-\lambda}$$

$$P(1) = \frac{\lambda^2 e^{-\lambda}}{2!} + \frac{\lambda^3 e^{-\lambda}}{3!}$$

$$P(2) = \frac{\lambda^4 e^{-\lambda}}{4!} + \frac{\lambda^5 e^{-\lambda}}{5!}$$

etc.

for k = 3

$$P(0) = e^{-\lambda} + \lambda e^{-\lambda} + \frac{\lambda^2 e^{-\lambda}}{2!}$$

$$P(1) = \frac{\lambda^3 e^{-\lambda}}{3!} + \frac{\lambda^4 e^{-\lambda}}{4!} + \frac{\lambda^5 e^{-\lambda}}{5!}$$

etc.

When k = 1, the simple Poisson distribution results.

Determining the parameters k and λ of this distribution is not a straightforward procedure. The best way of determining k is by means of the nomograph of Figure 1. This nomograph is entered with the mean, m, and the variance, s^2, of the observed data, and the closest value of k is read. While it is possible to read λ from Figure 1, this equation (3) is more reliable

$$\lambda = km + \frac{1}{2}(k - 1).$$

Poisson terms with parameter λ are then computed or read

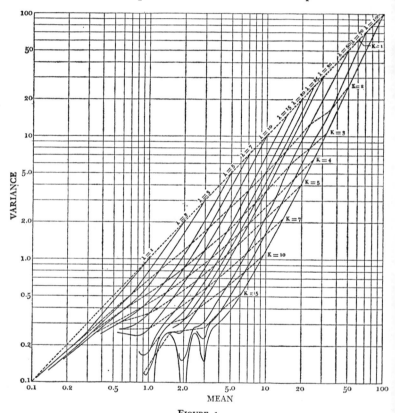

FIGURE 1.
Nomograph for estimating parameter k for generalized Poisson distribution.

Source: Haight, Frank A., Whisler, Bertram F., and Mosher, Walter W., Jr., "New Statistical Method for Describing Highway Distribution of Cars," *Proceedings of Highway Research Board*, Vol. 40, 1961, pp. 557-563.

from tables $(4, 5)$ and successive groups of k terms are summed to obtain the generalized-Poisson terms.

Example 13 shows a case where freeway traffic exhibits a variance much lower than the mean. Part a shows the observed data, along with the computation of the sample mean and the sample variance. The parameters k and λ are estimated as 2 and 15.438 respectively.

Part b exhibits the fitting of a generalized-Poisson curve to the data. Part c gives the results of a χ^2 test on the fit.

Example 13 Part a

VEHICLE ARRIVALS—INTERSTATE HIGHWAY 494 AT 24TH AVENUE*
Median Lane—A.M. Peak

15-second intervals

Number of cars per interval x_i	Observed frequency f_i	Total cars observed $f_i x_i$	$f_i x_i^2$
0			
1			
2			
3	3	9	27
4	0	0	0
5	8	40	200
6	10	60	360
7	11	77	539
8	10	80	640
9	11	99	891
10	9	90	900
11	1	11	121
12	1	12	144
	64	478	3822

$$m = \frac{478}{64} = 7.469$$

$$s^2 = \frac{3822 - \frac{(478)^2}{64}}{63} = 3.999$$

$$s^2/m = 0.535$$

From nomograph of Figure 1, with $k \approx 2$

$$\lambda = km + \frac{1}{2}(k-1) = 2(7.469) + 0.5 = 15.438$$

* Data by courtesy of Minnesota Department of Highways.

Example 13 Part b

Number of cars per interval x_i	$p(2x_i)$	$p(2x_i + 1)$	Probability $P(x_i)$	Theoretical frequency $64\,P(x_i)$
0	0.0000	0.0000	0.0000	0.0
1	0.0000+	0.0000+	0.0001	0.0
2	0.0005	0.0015	0.0020	0.1
3	0.0039	0.0084	0.0123	0.8
4	0.0162	0.0275	0.0437	2.8
5	0.0423	0.0590	0.1013	6.5
6	0.0755	0.0894	0.1649	10.6
7	0.0983	0.1010	0.1993	12.8
8	0.0974	0.0885	0.1859	11.9
9	0.0760	0.0619+	0.1380	8.8
10	0.0480	0.0354	0.0834	5.3
>10			0.0691	4.4

For $k = 2$, $m = 7.469$, $\lambda = 15.438$

Note: Column 4 is the sum of columns 2 and 3.

Example 13 Part c

Number of cars per interval x_i	Observed frequency $f(x_i)$	Theoretical frequency $F(x_i)$	$\dfrac{f(x_i)^2}{F(x_i)}$
⩽ 5	11	10.2	11.9
6	10	10.6	9.4
7	11	12.8	9.5
8	10	11.9	8.4
9	11	8.8	13.8
⩾10	11	9.7	12.5
	$\overline{64}$	$\overline{64.0}$	$\overline{65.5}$

$$\chi^2 = 65.5 - 64.0 = 1.5$$
$$v = 6 - 3 = 3$$

$$\chi^2_{.05,3} = 7.8$$

The Binomial Distribution

The binomial distribution is described in detail in Appendix C. Stated in the form most useful for traffic purposes, it is

$$P(x) = C^n_x p^x (1 - p)^{n-x}$$

where p = the probability that one car arrives

For the binomial distribution,

$$m = \text{mean} = np$$
$$s^2 = np(1 - p).$$

For estimating the parameters $\hat{p}$ and $\hat{n}$, used to obtain a binomial fit (6),

$$\hat{p} = (m - s^2)/m$$
$$\hat{n} = m/p = m^2/(m - s^2)$$

Fitting may be accomplished by direct computation or by the use of tables (7). Example 14 shows the fitting of a binomial distribution to the data used in Example 13.

Alternate Fitting Procedure for Generalized-Poisson Distribution

In Example 13 the parameter k was 2, and the generalized-Poisson distribution was fitted by summing 2 simple Poisson terms to obtain each generalized-Poisson term. Another fitting procedure for the generalized-Poisson distribution makes use of the normalized incomplete gamma function.* When this fitting procedure is used, k is not restricted to integer values.

---

* The normalized incomplete gamma function may be stated (8, 9, 10):

$$I(u, p) = \frac{\int_0^\lambda e^{-\lambda} \lambda^p d\lambda}{\int_0^\infty e^{-\lambda} \lambda^p d\lambda}$$

where: $p = (x + 1) k - 1$
$u = \lambda/(p + 1)^{1/2}$

Example 14

BINOMIAL DISTRIBUTION FITTED TO DATA OF EXAMPLE 13
(Interstate Highway 494 at 24th Avenue)
(Median Lane—A.M. Peak)
(15-second intervals)

Number of cars per interval x_i	Observed frequency f_i	Theoretical frequency F_i	f_i/F^2
< 3	0 ⎫	0.3 ⎫	
3	3 ⎬ 11	1.0 ⎬ 10.4	11.63
4	0 ⎪	2.9 ⎪	
5	8 ⎭	6.2 ⎭	
6	10	9.8	10.20
7	11	12.3	9.84
8	10	12.1	8.26
9	11	9.4	12.87
10	9 ⎫	5.8 ⎫	
11	1 ⎬ 11	2.8 ⎬ 10.0	12.10
12	1 ⎪	1.0 ⎪	
>12	0 ⎭	0.4 ⎭	
	$\overline{64}$	$\overline{64.0}$	$\overline{64.90}$

$$\Sigma f^2/F - n = 64.90 - 64 = 0.90 \qquad m = 7.469$$

$$v = 6 - 3 = 3 \qquad s^2 = 3.999$$

$$\chi^2_{.05} = 7.81 \qquad s^2/m = 0.535$$

Since $0.90 < 7.81$, $\qquad \hat{p} = 0.46$

Accept at 0.05 level $\qquad \hat{n} = 16.08$

The procedure for fitting generalized-Poisson distribution using tables of the incomplete gamma function is as follows:

1. Enter graph (Figure 1) with mean and variance. Select value for k. The value of k need not be an integer but may be any value greater than 1. (If k = 1, the usual "simple" form of the Poisson should be used.)
2. Compute λ from the relationship

$$\lambda = mk + (k - 1)/2$$

3. Form the table:

x	(p + 1)	u	p	I(u, p)	1 − I(u, p)	P(x)
0						
1						
2						
3						
etc.						

The following equations are used:

$$(p + 1) = (x + 1)k$$

$$u = \lambda/(p + 1)^{1/2}$$

$$p = (p + 1) - 1$$

4. Values of I(u, p) are obtained from tables (10)
5. The entries in the column [1 − I(u, p)] are the cumulative probabilities. The probabilities of the individual values of x, i.e., P(x), are obtained by subtraction:

$$P(0) = 1 - I(u, p)_0$$

$$P(x) = [1 - I(u, p)_x] - [1 - I(u, p)_{x-1}]$$

$$= I(u, p)_{x-1} - I(u, p)_x$$

Example 15 demonstrates the fitting of the generalized-Poisson distribution by means of tables of the normalized incomplete gamma distribution. For purposes of comparison, the same data as used in Examples 13 and 14 have been used here. Though there are some variations between the results of Example 13 and those of Example 15, the fit of Example 15 is acceptable by the χ^2 test.

When integer values of k are used, the method of fitting used in Example 13 (summing Poisson terms) is easier than that using the gamma distribution. The Poisson terms can be computed by hand, generated by a simple computer program, or looked up in readily available tables. The gamma distribution values require a very complex computer program; the tables are not readily available and interpolation of the tables is very time consuming.

In some cases one is tempted to use non-integer values of k

Example 15

GENERALIZED-POISSON DISTRIBUTION FITTED TO DATA OF EXAMPLE 13 BY METHOD OF INCOMPLETE GAMMA FUNCTION

(Vehicle Arrivals, Interstate 494 at 24th Avenue)
(Median Lane, P.M. Peak)

Number of cars per interval x_i	$(x_i + 1)k$ $= (p + 1)$	$\lambda/(p+1)^{1/2}$ $= u$	p	$I(u,p)^*$	$P(x)$	Theoretical frequency F	Observed frequency f	f^2/F
0	2	10.9	1	1.000	.000			
1	4	7.7	3	1.000	.000			
2	6	6.3	5	.998	.002	0.1 ⎫	⎫	
3	8	5.5	7	.987	.011	0.7 ⎬ 9.5	3 ⎬	
4	10	4.9	9	.945	.042	2.7 ⎪	0 ⎬ 11	12.7
5	12	4.5	11	.851	.094	6.0 ⎭	8 ⎭	
6	14	4.1	13	.669	.182	11.7	10	8.5
7	16	3.9	15	.477	.192	12.3	11	9.8
8	18	3.6	17	.289	.188	12.0	10	8.3
9	20	3.5	19	.150	.139	8.9	11	13.6
10	22	3.3	21	.069	.081	5.2 ⎫ 9.6	9 ⎫ 11	12.6
>10					.069	4.4 ⎭	2 ⎭	
						64.0	64	65.5

$k = 2$

$v = 6 - 2 = 4$

$65.5 - 64.0 = 1.5$

$\chi^2_{.05} = 2.37$

in order to obtain a closer fit. In such cases the use of the gamma distribution is necessary. Before expending the effort needed to interpolate the gamma distribution tables, however, the engineer should note the modest improvement Haight shows as a result of using a non-integer value of k (3).

PREDICTION OF ARRIVALS FROM HOURLY VOLUME

For conditions in which the Poisson distribution applies—i.e., under conditions of "free flow"—it is possible to compute the probability of 0, 1, 2, ... , h vehicles arriving per time interval of t seconds provided the hourly volume, V, is known:

t = length of time interval in seconds

V = hourly volume

n = number of intervals (per hour)

$$= \frac{3600}{t}$$

m = average number of vehicles per interval

$$= \frac{V}{\frac{3600}{t}} = \frac{Vt}{3600}$$

Then the probability, $P(x)$, that x vehicles will arrive during any interval is:

$$P(x) = \frac{m^x e^{-m}}{x!} = \frac{1}{x!} \left(\frac{Vt}{3600} \right)^x e^{-\frac{Vt}{3600}}$$

The hourly frequency, F_x, of intervals containing x vehicles is:

$$F_x = n\, P(x) = \left(\frac{3600}{t} \right) \frac{1}{x!} \left(\frac{Vt}{3600} \right)^x e^{-\frac{Vt}{3600}}$$

If the period under consideration is different from an hour, the 3600 in the first parentheses would be replaced by the appropriate length of time in seconds. The value V, however, would still be the hourly volume.

Summary

This chapter has presented various counting distributions suitable for representing traffic data, procedures for fitting the distributions to observed data, and procedures for testing the goodness of fit. Table 1 summarizes the selection of a suitable distribution, based on the ratio of the variance to the mean of the observed data.

Attention is called to the fact that the number of observations (e.g., the number of time periods) should be on the order of 50 or greater. It should be noted that the minimum length of the observation interval may be a function of the method of measurement. For example, if the method of measurement does not permit a resolution to 0.1 second or less, attempts to use a one-second counting period may lead to inconclusive or even spurious results. Methods of computation are discussed in Chapter V.

Table 1. Guide to Selection of Distribution

Range of ratio: $\dfrac{variance}{mean}$	Situations where this condition may prevail	Suggested distribution
>1	Variation in mean value; Cyclic fluctuation	Negative binomial distribution
≈ 1	Essentially random behavior	Poisson distribution
<1	Congested flow*	1. Generalized-Poisson distribution 2. Binomial distribution

* Pak-Poy suggests (11) that the critical volume is approximately the practical capacity as computed by the 1950 Capacity Manual (12).

Note: At the present state of the art, it is impossible to give definitive values for the ratios of variance to mean at which the Poisson distribution fails to fit. However, Figure 1 provides a basis for selecting the appropriate value of k in the generalized-Poisson Distribution.

The χ^2 test has been presented for testing the goodness of fit by comparing observed and theoretical frequencies in each category (when the χ^2 test is used on continuous distributions, they must be segmented into discrete categories). The χ^2 test is suitable for use even in cases where population parameters are estimated from the data.

In the performance of a goodness-of-fit test, the fit is accepted or rejected on the basis of some preselected significance level α.* In selecting this significance level the engineer takes the risk that the proportion α of all distributions rejected will in fact truly represent the observed data. It should be noted, however, that an acceptable test is less conclusive than one which fails. The rigorous interpretation of an acceptable test should be, "There is no evidence to indicate that the observed data did not come from the population represented by the distribution."

Once a distribution has been accepted as representing an observed situation, thereafter the distribution may be used for prediction and design.

General Usefulness of Poisson Distribution

In closing this discussion of counting distributions it seems appropriate to call attention to some pertinent remarks by Underwood (*13*):

"While less accurate than the more sophisticated distributions that have been proposed by various workers, the virtue of the Poisson distribution is that it is relatively easy to use. Bearing in mind the various other assumptions and approximations that often must be used in road traffic calculations, it is believed that the Poisson approximation is sufficiently accurate to use for many practical problems, provided it is realized that errors increase as the volume increases."

---

* Popular values of α are: 0.01 (1%), 0.05 (5%), and 0.10 (10%). Perhaps the most popular is 0.05 (5%). In the absence of other criteria, it is suggested that the engineer use 0.05 (5%).

REFERENCES FOR CHAPTER II

1. Wine, R. L., *Statistics for Scientists and Engineers*, Prentice-Hall, 1964, pp. 179–182.
2. Williamson, Eric and Bretherton, Michael H., *Tables of the Negative Binomial Probability Distribution*, Wiley, 1963, pp. 9–11.
3. Haight, Frank A., Whisler, Bertram F., and Mosher, Walter W., Jr., "New Statistical Method for Describing Highway Distribution of Cars," *Proceedings of Highway Research Board*, Vol. 40, 1961, pp. 557–563.
4. Molina, E. C., *Poisson's Exponential Binomial Limit*, Van Nostrand, 1945.
5. General Electric Co., Defense Systems Dept., *Tables of Individual and Cumulative Terms of the Poisson Distribution*, Van Nostrand, 1962.
6. Drew, D. R., *Traffic Flow Theory and Control*, McGraw Hill, 1968, p. 130.
7. a. Harvard University Computation Laboratory, *Tables of the Cumulative Binomial Probability Distribution*, Harvard University Press, 1955.
   b. Weintraub, Sol, *Tables of the Cumulative Binomial Probability Distribution for Small Values of p*, Collier-Macmillan Ltd. (London), 1963.
8. Haight, Frank A., "The Generalized Poisson Distribution," *Annals of the Institute of Statistical Mathematics* (Tokyo), Vol. 11, 1959, pp. 101–105.
9. Whittlesey, J. B., "Incomplete Gamma Functions for Evaluating Erlang Process Probabilities," *Mathematics of Computation*, Vol. 17, No. 81, January 1963, pp. 11–17.
10. Pearson, Karl, *Tables of the Incomplete Gamma Function*, Cambridge University Press, 1957.
11. Pak-Poy, P. G., "The Use and Limitation of the Poisson Distribution in Road Traffic," *Proceedings of Australian Road Research Board*, Vol. 2, 1964, pp. 223–247.
12. Highway Research Board, *Highway Capacity Manual*, 1950.
13. Underwood, R. T., Discussion of Pak-Poy paper, *Proceedings of Australian Road Research Board*, Vol. 2, 1964, p. 243.

Chapter III

INTERVAL DISTRIBUTIONS

The previous discussions of arrival rate, etc., have dealt with counting distributions for discrete events (arrivals of cars) within a given time interval. The distribution of gaps (time spacing) between vehicles is a continuous variable and is treated by means of interval distributions. Of these distributions, the best known is the (negative) exponential distribution.

THE EXPONENTIAL DISTRIBUTION

In Chapter II it is shown that the value of "m" in the Poisson distribution may be replaced as follows:

$$m = \frac{Vt}{3600}$$

where V = hourly volume

t = length of each observation in seconds.

Thus

$$P(x) = \left(\frac{Vt}{3600}\right)^x \frac{e^{-\frac{Vt}{3600}}}{x!}$$

$$P(o) = e^{-\frac{Vt}{3600}}$$

If there are no vehicles in a particular interval of length t, then there will be a gap of at least t seconds between the last previous vehicle and the next vehicle. In other words, P(o) is also the probability of a gap equal to or greater than t seconds. This may be expressed:

$$P(g \geq t) = e^{-\frac{Vt}{3600}}$$

From this relationship it may be seen that (under conditions of random flow) the number of gaps greater than any given value will be distributed according to an exponential curve. (Though most correctly a "negative exponential," this is usually known as simply an exponential distribution.)

In the above equation m or $\dfrac{Vt}{3600}$ is the mean of the arrival (counting) probability distribution. If we set

$$m = \frac{t}{T}$$

then

T = the mean of the interval (gap) probability distribution.

Thus, the probability of a gap equal to or greater than t may be written:

$$P(g \geq t) = e^{-\frac{t}{T}}$$

Example 16 presents the fitting of an exponential distribution to data observed on the Arroyo Seco Freeway (now the Pasadena Freeway). The observations included 214 intervals totaling 1753 seconds. Thus,

$$T = \frac{1753}{214} = 8.19 \text{ seconds}$$

$$m = \frac{t}{T} = \frac{t}{8.19} = 0.122t$$

$$P(g \geq t) = e^{-0.122t}$$

G = (Expected number of gaps $\geq$ t) = $214e^{-0.122t}$

It will be noted that the χ^2 test shows the fit to be acceptable at

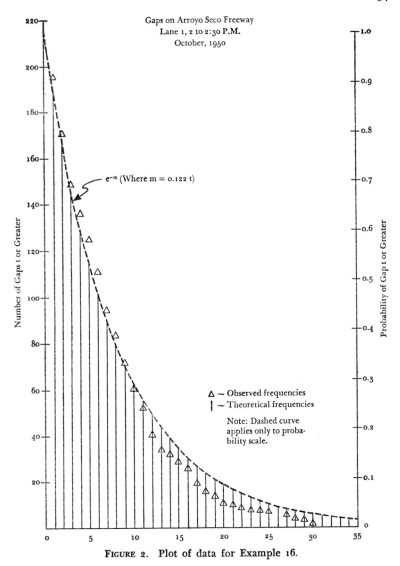

FIGURE 2. Plot of data for Example 16.

the 5% level. Figure 2 is a graphical presentation of the observed and theoretical data.*

* It should be noted that $\dfrac{Vt}{3600}$, the number of vehicles arriving during an in-

Example 16

INTER-VEHICLE GAPS—ARROYO SECO FREEWAY

Gap t Seconds	Observed Cumulative Frequency ≥ t	Observed Individual Frequency (f)	Theoretical Probability (Cumulative)	Absolute Difference Probability	Theoretical Frequency F	f^2/F
0	214		1.000	0.000		
1	185	29	0.894	0.030	22.7	37.0
2	171	14	0.799	0.000	20.3	9.7
3	149	22	0.715	0.019	18.0	26.9
4	136	13	0.639	0.003	16.3	10.4
5	125	11	0.571	0.013	14.5	8.3
6	111	14	0.511	0.008	12.8	15.3
7	95	16	0.457	0.013	11.6	22.1
8	84	11	0.408	0.015	10.5	11.5
9	72	12	0.365	0.029	9.2	15.7
10	61	11	0.326	0.041	8.3	14.6
11	52	9	0.292	0.049	7.3	11.1
12	40	12	0.261	0.073	6.7	21.5
13	34	6	0.233	0.084	5.9	6.1
14	32	2	0.208	0.058	5.4	0.7
15	29	3 } 6	0.186	0.050	4.7 } 8.8	—
16	26	3	0.167	0.046	4.1	4.1

Class						
17	19	7 ⎫10	0.149	0.060	3.8 ⎫7.2	13.9
18	16	3 ⎭	0.133	0.058	3.4 ⎭	
19	14	2 ⎫5	0.119	0.054	3.0 ⎫5.8	4.3
20	11	3 ⎭	0.106	0.055	2.8 ⎭	
21	10	1 ⎫	0.095	0.048	2.4 ⎫	1.4
22	9	1 ⎬3	0.085	0.043	2.1 ⎬6.4	
23	8	1 ⎭	0.076	0.039	1.9 ⎭	
24	8	0 ⎫	0.068	0.031	1.7 ⎫	3.9
25	7	1 ⎪	0.061	0.029	1.5 ⎪	
26	7	0 ⎪	0.054	0.022	1.5 ⎪	
27	6	1 ⎬8	0.049	0.021	1.1 ⎬16.3	
28	4	2 ⎪	0.043	0.024	1.3 ⎪	
29	3	1 ⎪	0.039	0.025	0.9 ⎪	
30	1	2 ⎪	0.035	0.030	0.8 ⎪	
≥31	0	1 ⎭	0.031	0.031	1.1 ⎭	
Σ	214	214	214.0		214.0	238.3

$$\chi^2_{\text{test}} = 238.3 - 214.0 = 24.3$$

$$\upsilon = 19 - 2 = 17$$

$$\chi^2_{.05} = 27.6$$

∴ Fit acceptable at 5% level.

The fact that the fit of the exponential distribution to the data is marginal may be thought of as typical for automobile traffic. One phenomenon that causes the interval (gap) distribution to depart from the exponential distribution is the fact that cars have a physical size and drivers have a tendency to maintain a minimum following distance. Thus, while very short gaps are theoretically possible, they cannot be observed in a *single* lane of traffic. When several lanes are being observed with no distinction as to which lane a vehicle occupies, very small gaps can be observed, but their frequency will be less than would be predicted by the exponential distribution.

In many cases there may be an advantage to accepting some sacrifice of accuracy for the sake of simplicity. Because of this, the exponential distribution finds reasonably wide use. The exponential is fitted by computing the mean interval T, and then using tables *(1)* to obtain values $e^{-\frac{t}{T}}$ for various values of t. (See column 3 of Example 16.)

SHIFTED EXPONENTIAL DISTRIBUTION

One approach to the treatment of the phenomena of physical length of cars and minimum following distance by drivers is the use of the shifted exponential distribution. In the previous section the discussion centered around the form of the exponential distribution

$$P(g \geqslant t) = e^{-\frac{t}{T}}.$$

This is illustrated graphically in Figure 3a (which is taken from reference 2).

terval, and G, the number of gaps equal to or greater than some specified value t, are discrete variables. That is, the number of vehicles or the number of gaps can take on only integral values 0, 1, 2, . . . etc. Probability, P(x) and time, t, on the other hand, are continuous variables and can take on fractional values. This is illustrated in Figure 2, where the theoretical frequencies are represented by bars and the probability curve is represented by a continuous dashed curve.

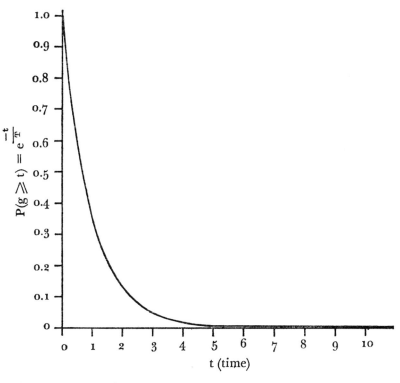

FIGURE 3a. Probability of gaps (headways) equal to or greater than t, as treated by the exponential distribution.

Consider the form

$$P(g < t) = 1 - e^{-\frac{t}{T}}$$

This form is sketched in Figure 3b (from Reference 2). If now we exclude gaps of size smaller than some value, say τ, this situation can be represented by shifting the exponential distribution to the right by an amount τ as illustrated in Figure 3c (also from Reference 2). When this is done, the equation becomes

$$P(g < t) = 1 - e^{-(t-\tau)/(T-\tau)}$$

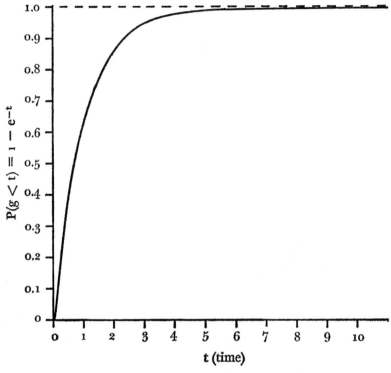

FIGURE 3b.   Probability of gaps (headways) less than t.

This is a very powerful practical tool* and is discussed in detail in Schuhl's study and Appendix L. Figure 4 illustrates a shifted exponential distribution fitted to field data.

THE ERLANG DISTRIBUTION

In discussing counting distributions it was found that the generalized-Poisson distribution can be used for a variety of levels of randomness by varying a parameter k from 1 (pure

---

* The practical use of the shifted exponential has been discussed by several writers. See for example Reference 2. Some writers have pointed out, however, that whereas shifting the exponential distribution assumes that very small intervals are impossible, there may be a more rigorous theoretical basis for using some other distribution which treats very small intervals as improbable but not impossible (3).

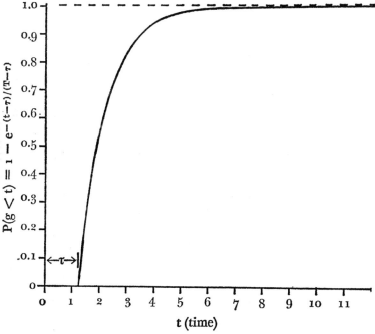

FIGURE 3c. Shifted exponential distribution to represent the probability of gaps (headways) less than t with a prohibition of gaps less than τ. (Average of observed gaps is T.)

randomness—i.e., simple Poisson) to infinity (completely regular, i.e., non-random). The corresponding distribution for intervals (gaps) is the Erlang distribution, named for the Danish mathematician who devoted many years to the study of telephone traffic. The cumulative Erlang distribution may be stated:*

$$P(g \geqslant t) = \sum_{i=0}^{k-1} \left(\frac{kt}{T}\right)^i \frac{e^{-\frac{kt}{T}}}{i!}$$

* Several writers have pointed out that to be strictly correct, one should use the gamma distribution. The Erlang distribution is a special case of the gamma distribution using integer values of k while the general form of the gamma distribution permits non-integer values of k. While the use of non-integer values of may at times result in a better fit, the complexity of the computation appears to more than offset the advantages. References 5, 6, and 7 discuss these matters.

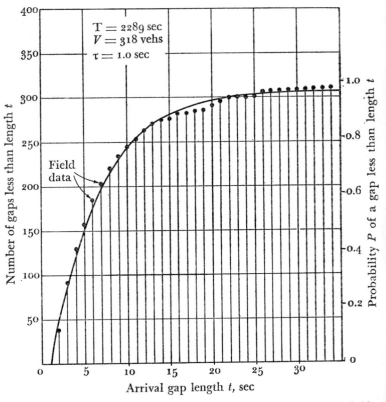

FIGURE 4. Shifted exponential fitted to field observations taken in Cambridge, Massachusetts. (From Figure 15.4, "Traffic System Analysis for Engineers and Planners," Wohl, M., and Martin, B. V. Copyright 1967 by McGraw-Hill, Inc. Used with permission of McGraw-Hill Book Company.)

When $k = 1$, this expression reduces to the exponential distribution. For $k = 2$

$$P(g \geq t) = \left[1 + \left(\frac{kt}{T} \right) \right] e^{-\frac{kt}{T}}$$

For $k = 3$

$$P(g \geq t) = \left[1 + \left(\frac{kt}{T} \right) + \left(\frac{kt}{T} \right)^2 \frac{1}{2!} \right] e^{-\frac{kt}{T}}$$

For $k = 4$

$$P(g \geqslant t) = \left[1 + \left(\frac{kt}{T} \right) + \left(\frac{kt}{T} \right)^2 \frac{1}{2!} + \left(\frac{kt}{T} \right)^3 \frac{1}{3!} \right] e^{-\frac{kt}{T}}$$

Here k is a parameter that determines the shape of the distribution. The value of k may be estimated from the mean (T) and variance (s^2) of the observed data, in the following manner:

$$k \approx \frac{T^2}{s^2}$$

THE KOLMOGOROV-SMIRNOV TEST FOR GOODNESS OF FIT

In addition to the χ^2 test, the Kolmogorov-Smirnov (K-S) test (8) is another technique for testing goodness of fit. The necessary calculations are relatively simple and, like the χ^2 test, it is nonparametric or distribution-free, (i.e., no assumption is made concerning the shape of the population from which the samples are drawn). The test is based on the simple measurement of the maximum vertical difference between the two cumulative distributions. This may be done graphically or it may be done in tabular form. It is necessary only to find the maximum absolute difference between the theoretical and observed cumulative distributions. This maximum difference is then compared with the tabulated or computed value of the K-S statistic. A table for obtaining values of the K-S statistic for various sample sizes and levels of significance is given in Appendix H.

The K-S test is particularly valuable in cases where the number of observations is small. However, this test cannot be used when the population parameters are estimated from the observations, inasmuch as the correction of the critical value because of such estimation is unknown.

Example 17A

ESTIMATION OF PARAMETERS FOR ERLANG DISTRIBUTION

Observed Headways
(Observations 2, 4, 6
... 48, 50)

x	x^2
0.9	0.81
2.1	4.41
2.5	6.25
3.8	14.44
1.4	1.96
1.1	1.21
2.9	8.41
1.8	3.24
1.2	1.44
1.0	1.00
1.1	1.21
2.0	4.00
2.1	4.41
2.5	6.25
4.6	21.16
1.1	1.21
5.7	32.49
3.1	9.61
2.3	5.29
3.5	12.25
0.9	0.81
5.6	31.36
0.8	0.64
1.7	2.89
1.4	1.96
57.1	191.71

$$T = 57.1/25 = 2.204$$

$$s^2 = \frac{1}{24}\left[191.71 - \frac{3260.41}{25}\right] = 2.554$$

Estimate of k: $\quad k = \dfrac{T^2}{s^2} = \dfrac{(2.204)^2}{2.554} = 1.99 \approx 2$

Example 17B

FITTING OF ERLANG DISTRIBUTION AND TESTING BY K-S METHOD

t	Observed Gaps* $\geq t$	Observed Relative Frequency	Erlang** Proba- bility	K-S Differ- ence	Theoret- ical Gaps $\geq t$
0	25	1.00	1.000	0.000	25.0
1	21	0.84	.720	0.120	
2	11	0.44	.462	0.022	
3	7	0.28	.246	0.034	
4	4	0.16	.125	0.035	
5	2	0.08	.061	0.019	
6	1	0.04	.026	0.014	
7	0	0.00	.015	0.035	

Maximum difference: 0.12

$$K\text{-}S_{.05,25}: 0.27$$

* Observations 1, 3, 5, . . . 47, 49 used

$$** \ P(g \geq t) = \left[1 + \frac{2t}{2.204}\right] e^{-\frac{2t}{2.204}}$$

Where adequate data are available, this restriction concerning parameter estimation may be overcome by the following procedure. One half of the data is used to estimate the parameters; the other half of the data is then used for fitting to the population represented by the parameters.

Example of the Erlang Distribution and the K-S Test

Example 17A shows the estimation of Erlang parameters using half of a set of field observations (observations 2, 4, ... 48, 50). The parameters estimated are k = 2 and T = 2.204. Example 17B shows the fit of this distribution to the other half of the field data (observations 1, 3, 5, ... 47, 49). The fit is tested by the K-S test and found acceptable at the 0.05 (5%) level. It should be noted that the Erlang distribution as given herein is in the inverse cumulative form analogous to the exponential distribution of Figure 3a.

Example 18 shows the effect of varying the parameter k.

Example 18

EFFECT OF VARYING ERLANG PARAMETER K

Theoretical Frequency of Gaps Greater than t

t	$k = 1$	$k = 2$	$k = 3$	$k = 4$	$k = 5$	Observed Odd values	Observed Even values
0	25.0	25.0	25.0	25.0	25.0	25	25
1	23.1	19.2	21.1	22.2	23.0	21	22
2	19.2	11.5	12.2	12.7	13.1	11	13
3	15.1	6.1	5.7	5.2	4.8	7	6
4	11.4	3.1	2.3	1.7	1.3	4	3
5	8.5	1.5	0.9	0.5	0.3	2	2
6	6.1	0.7	0.3	0.1		1	0
7	4.6	0.3	0.1			0	
8	3.1	0.1					
9	2.1						
10	1.5						

NOTES ON OTHER DISTRIBUTIONS

Because the Erlang distribution (and its special case—the exponential distribution) do not fit traffic gap data very well, several writers have described more complex distributions for such data. Buckley (6) has proposed a semi-random distribution which appears to have merit. Dawson has combined the good features of shifted-exponential and the Erlang distributions to form a hyper-Erlang distribution (9). Greenberg has suggested the use of the lognormal distribution for headway data (10). Such distributions are beyond the scope of this monograph.

REFERENCES FOR CHAPTER III

1. U.S. National Bureau of Standards, *Tables of the Exponential Function e^x*, Applied Mathematics Series–14, June 29, 1951.
2. Gerlough, D. L., "Traffic Inputs for Simulation on a Digital Computer," *Proceedings of Highway Research Board*, vol. 38, 1959, pp. 480–492.
3. Haight, F. A., Whisler, B. F., and Mosher, W. W., Jr., "New Statistical Method for Describing Highway Distribution of Cars," *Proceedings of Highway Research Board*, vol. 40, 1961, pp. 557–564.
4. Wohl, M., and Martin, B. V., *Traffic System Analysis for Engineers and Planners*, McGraw-Hill, 1967, p. 506.
5. Drew, D. R., "Application of Continuous Distributions to Traffic," *Traffic Engineering*, vol. 36, no. 4, January 1966, pp. 29–31.
6. Buckley, D. J., "Roadway Traffic Headway Distributions," *Proceedings of Australian Road Research Board*, vol. 1, 1962, pp. 153–187.
7. Blunden, W. R., Clissold, C. M., and Fisher, R. B., "Distribution of Acceptance Gaps for Crossing and Turning Maneuvers," *Proceedings of Australian Road Research Board*, vol. 1, 1962, pp. 188–205.
8. Massey, F. J., Jr., "The Kolmogorov–Smirnov Test for Goodness of Fit," *Journal of American Statistical Association*, Vol. 46, 1951, pp. 68–78.
9. Dawson, R. F., and Chimini, L. A., *The Hyperlang Probability Distribution—A Generalized Traffic Headway Model*, Highway Research Record, No. 230, 1968, pp. 1–14.
10. Greenberg, I., "The Log-Normal Distribution of Headways," *Australian Road Research*, vol. 2, no. 7, March, 1966, pp. 14–18.

Chapter IV

USE OF DISTRIBUTIONS IN DESIGN AND OTHER APPLICATIONS

To an engineer, the principal use of a mathematical model is in design. Probability distributions constitute one class of mathematical model—a class which permits the handling of random phenomena in a manner which allows the user to assess the risk involved in a particular decision. Therefore the engineer should be familiar with the use of probability distributions in design problems and in other decisions. Thus this chapter is devoted to examples of certain design and application problems.

CUMULATIVE POISSON DISTRIBUTION

In the previous discussions of the Poisson distribution the probability of exactly 0, 1, 2, . . . items per trial (or time interval) has been computed. In many design problems it is desirable to compute such values as the probability that the number of items (vehicles arriving) per trial is:

1. c or fewer
2. more than c
3. fewer than c
4. c or more

These probabilities involve the cumulative Poisson distribution and may be expressed as follows:

$$P(x \leqslant c) = \text{Probability that } x \leqslant c = \sum_{x=0}^{c} P(x) = \sum_{x=0}^{c} \frac{m^x}{x!} e^{-m}$$

$$P(x > c) = 1 - P(x \leqslant c) = 1 - \sum_{x=0}^{c} \frac{m^x}{x!} e^{-m}$$

$$P(x < c) = P(x \leqslant c - 1) = \sum_{x=0}^{c-1} \frac{m^x}{x!} e^{-m}$$

$$P(x \geqslant c) = 1 - P(x < c) = 1 - \sum_{x=0}^{c-1} \frac{m^x}{x!} e^{-m}$$

EXAMPLES OF DESIGN PROBLEMS

Design of Special Traffic Signal Phase for Left Turns

Example 19

This example is patterned after one given by Adams (1). A single intersection is to be controlled by a pre-timed signal having a cycle of 55 seconds. From one of the approaches there is a left-turning movement amounting to 175 vehicles per hour. The layout of the intersection is such that two left-turning vehicles per cycle can be satisfactorily handled without difficulty, whereas three or more left-turning vehicles per cycle cause delays to other traffic. In what percent of the cycles would such delays occur?

$$m = \text{avg. left turns per cycle} = \frac{55 \times 175}{3600} = 2.67$$

$$P(x \geqslant 3) = 1 - \sum_{x=0}^{2} \frac{(2.67)^x}{x!} e^{-2.67}$$

$$= 1 - [0.069 + 0.185 + 0.247]$$

$$= 1 - 0.501 = 0.499$$

Answer: 49.9%

If a special left-turn phase is provided, in what percent of the cycles will this special feature be unnecessary by virtue of the fact that there is no left-turning vehicle?

$$P(o) = e^{-2.67} = 0.069$$

Answer: 6.9%

Thus, the feature is unneeded in about one out of 14 cycles.

Design of Left-Turn Lanes

Example 20

The California Division of Highways has applied the cumulative Poisson distribution to the design of left-turn lanes. The lanes are designed in such a manner that the number of cars desiring to make a left-turn during any signal cycle will exceed the lane capacity only 4% of the time—i.e., the probability of greater than a given number of cars is 0.04. This may be expressed:

$$0.04 = 1 - \sum_{x=0}^{c} \frac{1}{x!} \left(\frac{Lt}{3600} \right)^x e^{-\frac{Lt}{3600}}$$

Where: L = number of left-turning cars per hour
        t = length of signal cycle in seconds
        c = lane capacity (number of cars)

This relationship may be solved for c by accumulating terms in the right-hand member until the equation is satisfied.* A more direct method of computation, however, is to use tables or charts showing the various values for the cumulative Poisson distribution. Such a chart is included in Chapter V on Methods of Computation.

The values obtained are as follows:

* The equation will, in general, never be precisely satisfied because of the discrete nature of the Poisson distribution. There will be two values of c which nearly satisfy the relationship—one too large and one too small. It is then a matter of engineering judgment which to use.

REQUIRED STORAGE (Number of Vehicles)

Peak hour left-turn movements	60 second cycle	120 second cycle
100	4	7
200	7	12
300	9	16
400	12	20
500	14	24
600	16	28
700	18	32
800	20	36

Emergency System to Handle Vehicle Breakdowns in Tunnel

Example 21

Emergency equipment is being provided to handle vehicle breakdowns in a tunnel. There is concern over the possibility of simultaneous breakdowns of more than one vehicle. It is desired that probabilities of multiple breakdowns be assessed. In this case, "simultaneous" is defined as more than one breakdown during a 5-minute interval. The following data are available (2).

Condition	Total Breakdowns/Year
Peak 8 hr.	1,020
Off-peak 16 hr.	337

The calculation proceeds as follows:

Peak 8 hr.:

Total number of 5-minute periods per year

$$= \left(12 \, \frac{\text{periods}}{\text{hr}} \right) \left(\frac{8 \, \text{hr}}{\text{day}} \right) \left(\frac{365 \, \text{day}}{\text{yr}} \right) = 35,040$$

m = average occurrence of breakdown per 5-minute period

$$= \frac{1,020}{35,040} = 0.0291; \ e^{-0.0291} = 0.97132$$

$$P(x) = \frac{(0.0291)^x}{x!} \ e^{-0.0291}$$

Number of breakdowns in 5-minute interval	Probability of occurrence $P(x)$	Expected frequency of occurrence during year $F(x)$
0	0.97132	34,035.1
1	0.02827	990.1
2	0.00041	14.4
3	0.000004	0.1

Off-peak 16 hr:

Total 5-minute periods per year

$$= \left(12 \ \frac{periods}{hr}\right)\left(\frac{16 \ hr}{day}\right)\left(\frac{365 \ day}{yr}\right) = 70,080$$

$$m = \frac{337}{70,080} = 0.004809; \ e^{-0.004809} = 0.99521$$

x	$P(x)$	$F(x)$
0	0.99521	69,774.3
1	0.00478	335.0
2	0.00001	1.4

Accident Experience

Several writers have discussed the use of the Poisson distribution in accident analysis. The example which follows is taken from an unpublished paper by Belmont (3).

Ninety-three road sections each having average traffic less than 8,000 vehicles per day and average usage of less than 40,000 vehicle miles per day were combined to give 45 composite roads each carrying 35,000 to 40,000 vehicle-miles per day. The accident records of these roads were then compared using the Poisson distribution as follows:

Example 22a

SINGLE-CAR ACCIDENTS

Number of single-car accidents x	Number of roads observed f_x	Theoretical number of roads F_x		f_x^2/F_x
0	18	14.5		22.3
1	14	16.4		12.0
2	7	9.3		
3	4	3.5		
4	1	1.0		
5	0 } 13	0.2 } 14.1		12.0
6	0	0.04		
7	1	0.007		
≥8	0	0.001		
	45	45		46.3

$$m = \frac{51}{45} = 1.133$$

$$e^{-m} = 0.322$$

$$45e^{-m} = 14.5$$

$$\sum \frac{f_x^2}{F_x} = 46.3 - 45.0 = 1.3$$

$$v = 3 - 2 = 1$$

$$\chi_{.05}^2 = 3.84$$

Although the fit is acceptable at the 5% level, one might be suspicious of the road section having 7 accidents when the probability of this occurrence is $\dfrac{0.007}{45}$ or approximately 2×10^{-4}.

Eliminating this one suspected road section results in the following:

Example 22b

SINGLE-CAR ACCIDENTS

Number of single-car accidents x	Number of roads observed f_x	Theoretical number of roads F_x	f_x^2/F_x
0	18	16.2	20.0
1	14	16.2	12.1
2	7 ⎫	8.1 ⎫	
3	4 ⎪	2.7 ⎪	
4	1 ⎬ 12	0.7 ⎬ 11.6	12.4
≥5	0 ⎭	0.1 ⎭	
	44	44.0	44.5

$$m = \frac{44}{44} = 1.000$$

$$e^{-m} = 0.368$$

$$44e^{-m} = 16.2$$

$$\sum \frac{f_x^2}{F_x} = 44.5 - 44.0 = 0.5$$

$$\upsilon = 3 - 2 = 1$$

$$\chi_{.05}^2 = 3.84$$

Since there is no evidence (at the 5% level of significance) that there is a difference between the observed and the theoretical data, one may reasonably assume that each of these 44 roads has the same accident potential. Thus, among road sections from this group, any section is as likely as any other to have from zero to four accidents per year; a section which has four accidents is no more dangerous than one having no accidents, the occurrences being simply the operation of chance.

When only two roads or intersections are to be compared as to accident potential, the following technique (4) may be used.

a. Compute u,

$$u = \frac{x_1 - x_2 - 1}{\sqrt{x_1 + x_2}}$$

x_1 = larger of observed values

x_2 = smaller of observed values

b. Compare the resulting value of u with the appropriate critical value selected from table. If the computed value of u is less than the critical value, the two roads or intersections may be considered to have the same accident potential.

Significance level	Critical value of u
0.01	2.58
0.05	1.96
0.10	1.64

Comparison of Accidents at Two Intersections

Example 23

Intersection 1: 6 accidents during year considered

2: 8 accidents during year considered

$x_1 = 8$ $\qquad x_2 = 6$

$$u = \frac{8 - 6 - 1}{\sqrt{8 + 6}} = 0.267$$

Since the computed value of u in Example 23 is less than the 5% significance level, there is no evidence of a difference in accident potential between the two intersections.

Design of Reservoir Area for Parking Garage

Example 24

In designing parking garages, especially those with attendant parking, it is necessary to provide a reservoir area for cars waiting to be parked (5, 6). If the reservoir area is too large, useful space is wasted; if the reservoir area is too small, cars may be backed up into the street. Inasmuch as cars arrive randomly, there is some risk that regardless of the size of reservoir selected, its capacity may be exceeded on occasion. The engineer would like to be able to specify the risk of such overflow. Use of the Poisson distribution makes this analysis possible.

The analysis begins with the use of the cumulative Poisson distribution to compute, for a specified probability level, the maximum number of cars arriving during a period. (In the calculations below, two probability levels are included—0.95 and 0.99, defining the risk the maximum number of arrivals will be exceeded as 5% and 1% respectively.)

Let m = mean rate of arrival

A = the maximum number of arrivals with a probability P (i.e. the probability that A will be exceeded is $1 - P$)

P = the specified probability that the reservoir will not overflow

The cumulative Poisson distribution

$$P(x \leqslant A) = \sum_{x=0}^{A} \frac{m^x e^{-m}}{x!}$$

is used. The terms for various values of x as defined by the right-hand side of the equation are accumulated until reaching the first value of the summation which just equals or exceeds the specified value of P. The corresponding value of x is taken as A.

The following table shows some typical results for the two levels of probability. Inasmuch as it is rare for the specified probability to be met exactly, actual probabilities are also shown.

Mean Arrival Rate	Specified Probability = 0.95		Specified Probability = 0.99	
	Maximum Number of Arrivals	Actual Probability	Maximum Number of Arrivals	Actual Probability
1	3	0.981	4	0.996
10	15	0.951	18	0.993
50	62	0.958	67	0.991
100	117	0.957	124	0.991
200	224	0.956	234	0.991
300	329	0.954	341	0.991

(Computations courtesy of M. J. Huber)

Next, the average rate of storage is subtracted from the maximum number of arrivals to give the maximum accumulation in the storage area for the specified level of probability.* In the table below, the average rate of storage is taken equal to the average rate of arrival. For a more detailed analysis, including cases where the storage rate equals 0.9, 0.95, 1.0, 1.05, and 1.10 times the average arrival rate, see the procedures given in Reference 6.

Mean Arrival Rate	Maximum number of arrivals less mean storage rate	
	Specified Prob. = 0.95	Specified Prob. = 0.99
1	2	3
10	5	8
50	12	17
100	17	24
200	24	34
300	29	41

The interpretation, using the third line of the above result

---

* The subtraction of the average rate of storage is based on the statement of Cox and Smith that "The service time may be assumed to be constant. This is always an idealization but, particularly in problems with very irregular patterns, it often gives adequate answers." (See Reference 7.)

as an example, is "if during a given period the average arrival rate and the average storage rate both equal 50, a reservoir area having a capacity of 12 may be expected to overflow 5% of the time; if the capacity is 17, overflow may be expected 1% of the time."

School Crossing Protection

Example 25

(This example is based on the report of a joint committee of the Institute of Traffic Engineers and the International Association of Chiefs of Police (*8*)).

In studying the natural gaps in traffic at school crossings the following assumptions may be made:

1. The walking speed of a child is 3.5 ft./sec.
2. There must be at least one opportunity of crossing per minute. (This implies a minimum of 60 opportunities per hour.)

On the basis of these assumptions it is desired to determine the critical volume for a street of a given width. The critical volume here refers to that volume above which special measures will be required for the safety of the child.

There are two approaches to this problem, and care must be exercised in the selection of the appropriate method. One approach is that of finding the number of gaps greater than the time t required for a child to cross the street. The expected number of gaps per hour will be the traffic volume, V, and the probability (fraction) of gaps equal to or greater than t is

$$P(g \geq t) = e^{-Vt/3600}.$$

Thus, the expected number of gaps per hour which are equal to or greater than t will be*

---

* Relationship (I) assumes that only one crossing can take place during any interval, regardless of the length of the interval. Thus, if there were only two cars per hour, resulting in two intervals, only two crossings could take place. This, of course, is not a practical solution.

$$Ve^{-\frac{Vt}{3600}} \qquad (I)$$

The other approach is to find the number of t-second intervals per hour which are free of cars. The number of t-second intervals per hour is 3600/t. The probability (fraction) of such intervals free of cars is

$$P(o) = \left(\frac{Vt}{3600}\right)^0 \frac{e^{-Vt/3600}}{o!} = e^{-Vt/3600}$$

Thus, the expected number of t-second intervals per hour which are free of cars will be

$$\left(\frac{3600}{t}\right)\left(e^{-\frac{Vt}{3600}}\right) \qquad (II)$$

When one considers the fact that a long gap may contain several t-second intervals during each of which there is opportunity to cross, this second approach seems more appropriate.

Introducing the second assumption (at least 60 opportunities to cross per hour),

$$\frac{3600}{t} e^{-\frac{V_c t}{3600}} = 60 \qquad \text{(from II)}$$

where V_c denotes the critical volume.

From the first assumption (walking speed = 3.5 ft/sec),

$$t = \frac{D}{3.5}$$

where D is the width of the street.

Substituting:

$$\frac{3600 \cdot 3.5}{D} e^{-\frac{V_c D}{3600 \cdot 3.5}} = 60$$

$$e^{-\frac{V_c D}{12,600}} = \frac{60D}{12,600} = \frac{D}{210}$$

Taking the natural logarithm of both sides:

$$\frac{-V_c D}{12,600} = \ln \frac{D}{210}$$

$$V_c = -\frac{12,600}{D} \ln \frac{D}{210}$$

Making use of the relationship

$$\ln x = \frac{\log x}{\log e} = \frac{\log x}{0.4343}$$

gives

$$V_c = -\frac{12,600}{D} \frac{1}{0.4343} \log \frac{D}{210}$$

or

$$V_c = -\frac{29,000}{D} (\log D - \log 210)$$

or

$$V_c = \frac{29,000}{D} (2.322 - \log D)$$

This equation has been adopted by the joint committee of the Institute of Traffic Engineers and the International Association of Chiefs of Police. Solution of the equation gives the following values:

Width of street (ft.):	25	50	75
Critical volume (v.p.h.):	1072	361	173

SUMMARY

This chapter has presented several examples related to designs or other decisions faced by the traffic engineer. All designs related to counts have used the Poisson distribution; all designs related to gaps have used the exponential distribution. Such usage is in line with the idea set forth in the last paragraph of Chapter II, namely, *for design* the inaccuracies of the Poisson [and the exponential] distribution are of the same magnitude as other approximations, and ease of computation justifies the simplified relationships. It should be noted, however, that *for simulation* where the objective is to study microscopic properties of traffic behavior, use of more precise distributions is usually necessary.

REFERENCES FOR CHAPTER IV

1. Adams, William F., "Road Traffic Considered as a Random Series," *Journal of Institution of Civil Engineers* (London), vol. 4, November 1936, pp. 121–130 +.
2. Edie, Leslie C., "Expectancy of Multiple Vehicular Breakdowns in a Tunnel," *Journal of Operations Research Society of America* (now called *Operations Research*) vol. 3, no. 4, November 1955, pp. 513–522.
3. Belmont, D. M., *The Use of the Poisson Distribution in the Study of Motor Vehicle Accidents,* Technical Memorandum No. B-7, Institute of Transportation and Traffic Engineering, University of California, June 20, 1952.
4. Hald, A., *Statistical Theory with Engineering Applications,* John Wiley and Sons, Inc., 1952, pp. 725–726.
5. Capelle, D. G., Cleveland, D. E., and Rankin, W. W. (editors), *An Introduction to Highway Transportation Engineering,* Institute of Traffic Engineers, 1968, pp. 94–95.
6. Ricker, Edmund R., *Traffic Design of Parking Garages,* The Eno Foundation for Highway Traffic Control, 1957, p. 51.
7. Cox, D. R., and Smith, Walter L., *Queues,* London, Methuen, and New York, John Wiley and Sons, Inc., 1961, p. 19.
8. "Report on Warrants for Traffic Officers at School Intersections," *Proceedings, Institute of Traffic Engineers,* vol. 18, 1947, pp. 118–130.

Chapter V

METHODS OF COMPUTATION

While methods of computation have been indicated as each distribution has been described, techniques for many of the distributions are summarized here. When tables are available to the engineer, these usually represent a convenient method of computation (see References $1-9$). However, many of the tables are of such specialized nature that they are not often found in the average engineering office. In such cases slide rule calculations may be made using the recursion formulas given herein. For such computations it should be noted that values of e^x and e^{-x} can be obtained by a slide rule having log-log scales.

With the increasing availability of electronic computers, many engineers have access to such equipment. In such cases, the computer programs of Appendix J may be found convenient.

Poisson Distribution

Computing Probabilities

The following is a review of the procedure of computing probabilities from the Poisson distribution:

1. Determine the parameter m. This parameter is the average number of occurrences. It may be determined from observed or assumed data. A trial may consist of an instantaneous observation, counting events during a time interval, counting events in a unit area, etc.

$$m = \frac{\text{Total number of events observed}}{\text{Total number of trials or time intervals, etc.}}$$

2. Once m has been determined, the probability of x events

occurring at any trial (during any time interval) is computed from the formula

$$P(x) = \frac{m^x e^{-m}}{x!}$$

where $x! = x(x - 1)(x - 2)\ldots 3 \cdot 2 \cdot 1$

Computation may be performed in a variety of ways. Table II lists a number of tables that can be helpful in obtaining values of e^{-m} or Poisson terms.

When calculation is to be performed by slide rule, by computer program, or by other direct computation process, the following relationships are helpful.

$$P(0) = e^{-m} \qquad (1)$$

$$\frac{P(x)}{P(x - 1)} = \frac{\dfrac{m^x}{x!} e^{-m}}{\dfrac{m^{(x-1)}}{(x - 1)!} e^{-m}} \qquad (2)$$

From (2) $$P(x) = \frac{m}{x} P(x - 1) \qquad x \geqslant 1 \qquad (3)$$

Thus, from (1) and (3) it follows that

$$P(0) = e^{-m}$$

$$P(1) = \frac{m}{1} P(0)$$

$$P(2) = \frac{m}{2} P(1)$$

$$P(3) = \frac{m}{3} P(2) \qquad \text{etc.}$$

Equations of the type of (3) are known as "recursion formulas."

Slide Rule Calculations of the Poisson Distribution

The value of e^x can be found by means of a log-log-duplex slide rule; e^{-x} is, of course, the reciprocal of e^x. Having obtained

e^{-x} by slide rule or from tables, the individual terms of the Poisson distribution may be obtained by means of using the recursion formula (3).

Cumulative Poisson Distribution

Probabilities following the cumulative Poisson distribution may be computed:

by summing the individual Poisson terms
by using tables of the cumulative Poisson distribution
by using charts, such as Figure 5.

Chart of the Cumulative Poisson Distribution

Figure 5 is a modification of charts by Thorndike (*10*) and Working (*11*). The probability $P(x \leq c)$ is plotted against m with c as a parameter. The probability of x equal to or less than c is simply read from the curve. To obtain $P(x = c)$, the probability of exactly c, values are read from the chart for $x = c$ and for $x = (c - 1)$. The following relationship is then used:

$$P(x = c) = P(x \leq c) - P[x \leq (c - 1)]$$

BINOMIAL DISTRIBUTION

Where the binomial distribution is to be fitted, the parameters are estimated:

m = mean number of cars per observation
s^2 = variance of number of cars per observation

$$\hat{P} = (m - s^2)/m$$

$$\hat{n} = m/p = m^2/(m - s^2)$$

$$\hat{q} = 1 - \hat{p}$$

Probabilities may then be obtained from tables (see Table II) or may be computed using the following recursion relationships:

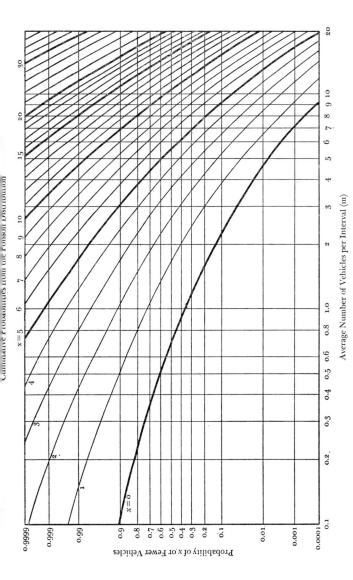

Modification of charts by F. Thorndike, *Bell System Technical Journal*, (October 1926) and H. Working,
A Guide to Utilization of the Binomial and Poisson Distributions, Stanford University Press, 1943.

FIGURE 5.   Chart of the Cumulative Poisson Distribution

TABLE II. TABLES TO AID COMPUTATION

Distribution	Reference	Format	Range*
Exponential	1	e^x, e^{-x}	x: 0.00 (.01) 10.00
	2	e^x	x: −2.5000 (.0001) 2.5000 (.001) 5.000 (.01) 10.00
	3	e^x, e^{-x}	x: 0 (.0001) .001 (.001) .010 (.01) .10 (.1) 1.0 (1.) 100
Poisson	4	Individual Terms $$\dfrac{a^x e^{-a}}{x!}$$	a: .001 (.001) .010 (.01) .30 (.1) 15. (1.) 100 x: as appropriate to give probability to 6 decimal places
		Cumulated Terms $$\sum_{x=c}^{\infty} \dfrac{a^x e^{-a}}{x!}$$	a: .001 (.001) .010 (.01) .30 (.1) 15. (1.) 100 c: as appropriate to give probability to 6 decimal places
	5	Individual Terms $$P(x) = \dfrac{e^{-U} U^x}{x!}$$ Cumulative Terms $$C(x) = \sum_{r=0}^{x} \dfrac{e^{-U} U^r}{r!}$$ Cumulative Terms $$D(x) = \sum_{r=x}^{\infty} \dfrac{e^{-U} U^r}{r!}$$	U: .0000010 (.000001) .0000015 (.0000005) .000015 .000015 (.000001) .00005 (.000005) .0005 .0005 (.00001) .001 (.00005) .005 .005 (.0001) .01 (.0005) .2 .2 (.001) .4 (.005) .5 .5 (.01) 1. (.05) 2. 2. (.1) 5. (.5) 10. 10. (1.) 100 (5.) 205 x and r: as appropriate to give probabilities to 8 decimal places

TABLE II. (*Continued*)

Distribution	Reference	Format	Range*
Binomial	6	Individual Terms $$\binom{n}{r} p^r (1-p)^{n-r}$$	p: .01 (.01) .50; n: 2 (1) 49; r: 0 (1) n − 1
		Partial Sums $$\sum_{s=r}^{n} \binom{n}{s} p^s q^{n-s}$$	p: .01 (.01) .50; n: 2 (1) 49; r: 1 (1) n
	7	$$\sum_{x=r}^{n} C_n p^x (1-p)^{n-x}$$	p: .01 (.01) .50, 1/16, 1/12, 1/8, 1/6, 3/16, 5/16, 1/3, 3/8, 5/12, 7/16; r: 0 (1) n; n: 1 (1) 50 (2) 100 (10) 200 (20) 500 (50) 1000
	8	$$\sum_{x=r}^{n} C_x^n p^x q^{n-x}$$	p: .00001; .0001 (.0001) .001 (.001) .100; n: 1 (1) 100
Negative Binomial	9	$$P(n) = \binom{n+k-1}{k-1} p^k q^n$$ $$F(n) = \sum_{r=0}^{n} \binom{r+k-1}{k-1} p^k q^r$$	p: .05; .10 (.02) .90; .95; for p = .05, k: .1 (.1) .5; for p = .50, k: 0.1 (.1) 2.5 (.5) 10.0 for p = .05, k: .1 (.1) .5; for p = .50, k: 0.1 (.1) 2.5 (.5) 10.0 for p = .50, k: 0.1 (.1) 2.5 (.5) 10.0 for p = .95, k: 2 (2) 50 (10) 200 n: as appropriate for probabilities to 6 decimal places

* The notation x: .002 (.001) .01 means that x goes from .002 to .01 in steps of .001.

$$P(0) = \hat{q}^n$$

$$P(x) = \frac{\hat{p}}{\hat{q}} \frac{n + 1 - x}{x} P(x - 1) \qquad x \geqslant 1$$

or

$$P(x + 1) = \frac{\hat{p}}{\hat{q}} \frac{n - x}{x + 1} P(x) \qquad x \geqslant 0$$

NEGATIVE BINOMIAL DISTRIBUTION

Where the negative binomial distribution is to be used, the parameters are estimated:

m = mean of observed data

s^2 = variance of observed data

$p = m/s^2$

$q = 1 - p$

$k = p\,m/q = m^2/(s^2 - m)$

Probabilities may then be obtained by the use of tables (see Table II) or computed directly, using the following recursion relationships:

$$P(0) = p^k$$

$$P(x) = \frac{x + k - 1}{x} q \cdot P(x - 1) \qquad x > 0$$

or

$$P(x + 1) = \frac{x + k}{x + 1} q \cdot P(x) \qquad x \geqslant 0$$

REFERENCES FOR CHAPTER V

1. *Handbook of Chemistry and Physics,* Chemical Rubber Co., or *Standard Mathematical Tables,* Chemical Rubber Co., various editions.
2. U.S. National Bureau of Standards, *Tables of the Exponential Function e^x,* Applied Mathematics Series, No. 14, June 29, 1951.

3. Hayashi, Keiichi, *Funfstellige Tafeln der Kreis- und Hyperbelfunktionen sowie der Funktionen e^x und e^{-x},* Walter de Gruyter & Co., (Berlin) 1944.

4. Molina, E. C., *Poisson's Exponential Binomial Limit,* Van Nostrand, 1942.

5. General Electric Co., Defense Systems Dept., *Tables of Individual and Cumulative Terms of the Poisson Distribution,* Van Nostrand, 1962.

6. U.S. National Bureau of Standards, *Tables of the Binomial Probability Distribution,* Applied Mathematics Series, No. 6, January 27, 1950.

7. Harvard University Computation Laboratory, *Tables of the Cumulative Binomial Probability Distribution,* Harvard University Press, 1955.

8. Weintraub, Sol, *Tables of the Cumulative Binomial Probability Distribution for Small Values of p,* Collier-Macmillan Ltd., 1963.

9. Williamson, Eric, and Bretherton, Michael H., *Tables of Negative Binomial Probability Distribution,* Wiley, 1963, pp. 9–11.

10. Thorndike, Frances, "Application of Poisson's Probability Summation," *Bell System Technical Journal* vol. 5, No. 4, October 1926, pp. 604–624.

11. Working, Holbrook, *A Guide to Utilization of the Binomial and Poisson Distributions,* Stanford University Press, 1943.

Probability Theory Applied to Vehicle Distribution on Two-Lane Highways

ANDRÉ SCHUHL

Reprinted with permission from *Travaux*, January 1955, revised and updated by the author. Translated from the French.

APPLICATIONS OF THEORY

A theoretical study of conditions affecting the traffic of vehicles on a highway requires the constant use of probability theory. On the one hand, the distribution of vehicles in each lane is in part a matter of chance. On the other hand, whenever one studies the behavior of any large number of individuals, inevitable departures from the laws which apply to their totality are found by statistical analysis to follow certain empirical and relatively stable patterns. These are, in effect, special laws of probability.

In particular, Poisson's law, applying to rare events, has thus far been the chief theoretical instrument for dealing with problems of vehicular traffic on two or three lane highways, especially the problems of determining the distribution of such traffic both in time and in space. This law, as is well known, assigns the value $e^{-N\theta} \dfrac{(N\theta)^n}{n!}$ to the probability that there are "n" vehicles in a time interval θ chosen at random, N being the average number of vehicles in unit time. The probability that there are no vehicles in this interval is

$$e^{-N\theta}$$

While the results yielded by this formula agree well enough with actual observation when the traffic density is low (a few dozen cars per hour per lane), they differ widely from reality when the density is significantly larger. The reasons for this discrepancy between theoretical prediction and the observed data are clear enough. But without going into any analysis of physical causes, it seems obvious that the gap between theory and actuality can be considerably narrowed. It is the object of this paper to show how this can be done.

We shall suppose that the entire set of spacings between successive vehicles consists of a number of distinct parts or sub-sets, each having distinct mean values and each obeying some Poisson-type law. For simplicity we consider just two sub-sets. Let the number of spacings per unit time for these two sets be respectively

$$\gamma N \text{ and } (1 - \gamma)\, N$$

with mean spacing-values of t_1 and t_2 seconds respectively, and with $t_1 < t_2$. We also suppose that the entire set of spacings is a set of random and independent elements.

Then the probability that there is no vehicle in an interval would be

$$e^{-\frac{\theta}{t_1}}$$

if all spacings were in the first sub-set and

$$e^{-\frac{\theta}{t_2}}$$

if they were all in the second sub-set.

Now the respective times covered by the two sub-sets are

$$\gamma N t_1 \quad \text{and} \quad 1 - \gamma N t_1,$$

and clearly

$$1 - \gamma N t_1 = (1 - \gamma)\, N t_2$$

Accordingly, the probability that there are no vehicles in an interval θ will be given by

$$P(\theta) = N\gamma t_1 e^{-\frac{\theta}{t_1}} + (1 - \gamma)\, N t_2 e^{-\frac{\theta}{t_2}} \tag{1}$$

with the relation

$$N\gamma t_1 + N(1 - \gamma)t_2 = 1,$$

which merely states that the N spacings cover unit time. Before proceeding further, it must be observed that the first set of spacings might apply to retarded vehicles which are prevented from passing by opposing traffic, and the second set to free-moving vehicles which are able to pass at will. As vehicles cannot be considered as mere points, two successive vehicles in the first set must necessarily be separated by a time interval having a positive lower bound ε. On the contrary, free-flowing vehicles having opportunities to pass may exhibit spacings equal to zero.

Hence the law of spacings which we use in practice is not formula (1), but rather the formula

$$P(\theta) = N\gamma t_1 e^{-\frac{\theta - \varepsilon}{t_1 - \varepsilon}} + N(1 - \gamma)t_2 e^{-\frac{\theta}{t_2}} \qquad \theta \geqslant \varepsilon \qquad (2)$$

For this formula to be correct, it is necessary that $\theta \geqslant \varepsilon$ which will always be the case practically, ε being very nearly one second of time. But if we suppose $\theta < \varepsilon$, then θ cannot contain one spacing of the first subset. There can be only one vehicle of this kind, with the probability $\frac{\theta}{t_1}$. The probability that there is no vehicle of this kind on the interval $\theta < \varepsilon$, will then be $1 - \frac{0}{t_1}$ and formula (2) must be written

$$P(\theta) = N\gamma(t_1 - \theta) + N(1 - \gamma)t_2 e^{-\frac{\theta}{t_2}} \qquad 0 \leqslant \theta \leqslant \varepsilon \qquad (2')$$

We must now examine the practical usefulness of the law embodied in formulas (1) and (2) in providing answers to various questions arising out of the study of traffic problems. They are considered in some detail in what follows.

We will suppose that the vehicles are represented by points on a straight line. We will apply the word "spacing" exclusively to the interval of time (or space) between two successive vehicles, while the word "interval" will be applied indistinctly to any interval of time (or space) between two points arbitrarily chosen on the line where the vehicles are represented, or between one such point and a vehicle.

FIRST QUESTION: *Probability of a Spacing Lying Between x and x + dx and Probability of a Spacing Longer than x.*

Suppose that p(x) dx is the probability of a spacing between x and x + dx. What then is the probability $P(\theta)$, that an interval θ chosen at random on the straight line, contains no points, all choices of θ on the line being equally probable?

Now the probability that the initial point A of the interval $AB = \theta$ will be in a spacing lying between x and x + dx is

$$kxp(x)dx,$$

k being defined by the condition

$$\int_0^\infty kxp(x)dx = 1,$$

which simply states that the point A necessarily falls in a spacing which lies between o and ∞ . The value of k is given by

$$k = \frac{1}{\int_0^\infty xp(x)dx} = \frac{1}{x_m} = N,$$

where x_m is the mean value of x.

If the interval $AB = \theta$ contains no points, L being the first point preceding A, and M the first one following A, with $LM = x$, it follows that $x \geqq \theta$ and that the initial point A lies between L and P, where $LP = x - \theta \geqq 0$. Now the probability that the interval $AB = \theta$ contains no points is the same as the probability that its initial point A lies between L and P, as seen in Figure 6. This probability is found from the above to be

$$k\left(\frac{x - \theta}{x}\right)xp(x)dx = N(x - \theta)p(x)dx$$

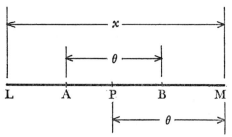

FIGURE 6. Illustration of the First Question

Hence upon integration over all values of x between θ and ∞ we have*

$$P(\theta) = \int_\theta^\infty N(x - \theta)p(x)dx = \int_\theta^\infty N\,dx \int_x^\infty P(x)dx \qquad (3)$$

From this we find by two successive differentiations, that

$$p(x) = \frac{1}{N}\frac{d^2\,P(x)}{dx^2}$$

Using this result, we find by taking the value of P(x) from (1) that in this case

$$p(x) = \frac{\gamma}{t_1}e^{-\frac{x}{t_1}} + \frac{1-\gamma}{t_2}e^{-\frac{x}{t_2}} \qquad (4)$$

while the total probability of a spacing longer than x is given by

$$\int_x^\infty p(x)dx = \gamma\,e^{-\frac{x}{t_1}} + (1-\gamma)e^{-\frac{x}{t_2}}. \qquad (5)$$

If on the other hand we take the value of P(x) furnished by (2) then

$$p(x) = \frac{\gamma}{t_1 - \varepsilon}e^{-\frac{\tau-\epsilon}{t_1-\epsilon}} + \frac{1-\gamma}{t_2}e^{-\frac{x}{t_2}} \qquad (x \geqslant \varepsilon) \qquad (6)$$

Which, when $0 \leqslant \chi < \varepsilon$, becomes

* In Equation (3) the second form of P(θ) results from an integration by parts of the first form. We can write

$$p(x) = -\frac{d}{dx}\int_x^\infty p(x)\,dx$$

and

$$\int_\theta^\infty (x - \theta)\,p(x)dx = -\left[(x - \theta)\int_x^\infty p(x)dx\right]_{x=\theta}^{x=\infty} + \int_\theta^\infty dx \int_x^\infty p(x)dx$$

$$p(x) = \frac{1 - \gamma}{t_2} e^{-\frac{x}{t_2}} \qquad (0 \leqslant x < \varepsilon) \qquad (6')$$

and

$$\int_x^\infty p(x)dx = \gamma e^{-\frac{x-\varepsilon}{t_1-\varepsilon}} + (1 - \gamma)e^{-\frac{x}{t_2}} \qquad (\chi \geqslant \varepsilon) \qquad (7)$$

Which, when $0 \leqslant x < \varepsilon$, becomes

$$\int_x^\infty p(x)dx = \gamma + (1 - \gamma)e^{-\frac{x}{t_2}} \qquad (0 \leqslant x < \varepsilon) \qquad (7')$$

It will be seen by examining the graphs of Figure 7 which has been taken from *Statistics With Applications to Highway Traffic Analyses* by Greenshields and Weida, that there is good agreement between the observed data and those furnished by formula (7). The legend on the diagram gives the actual numerical values of the various parameters used in this particular case. (See Appendix K).

Figure 8 gives another example, studied on a French road, showing how actual data are approximated by the theoretical formula. There were 312 spacings observed in a time period of 52 minutes, 45 seconds. Opposing traffic amounted to only 12 percent of the total flow.

SECOND QUESTION: *Probability That an Interval θ, Taken at Random, Contains no Vehicles, but is Bounded by a Vehicle on One Side.*

First, we clarify the significance of the iterated integrals occurring in formula (3).

If AB is placed at random on the spacing LM = x, AB can be empty only if A and B are between L and M.

Accordingly, $x \geqslant \theta$, and Figure 9 shows that the various cases in which AB contains no points, may be obtained by letting L range over all positions preceding A, and M over all positions following B.

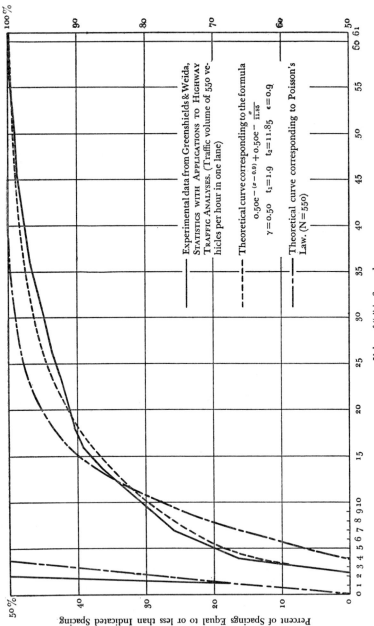

FIGURE 9. Observed Spacing and Theoretical Distributions

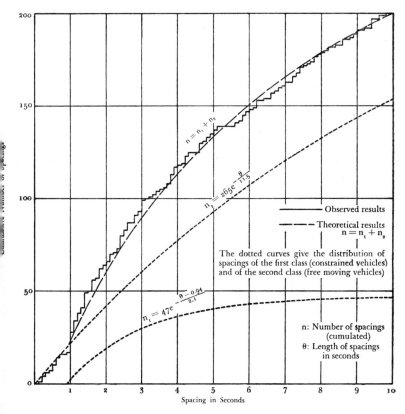

FIGURE 8. French Example of Observed Spacing and Theoretical Distribution

If B lies between M and M′, where MM′ = dv, and if kdv is the probability of this happening, then the probability that LM lies between u and u + du is the probability of a spacing

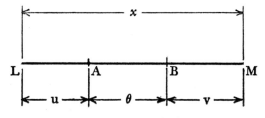

FIGURE 9. Illustration of the Second Question

$$u + \theta + v < x \leqslant u + du + \theta + v,$$

that is,

$$p(u + \theta + v)du$$

Therefore the total probability that L precedes A, M being given on dv, is

$$k \, dv \int_0^\infty p(u + \theta + v) \, du$$

Also the total probability that L precedes A $(u \geqslant 0)$ and that M follows B $(v \geqslant 0)$ is

$$\int_0^\infty k \, dv \int_0^\infty p(u + \theta + v)du$$

If we make the substitution

$$u + \theta + v = x,$$

this can be written in the form

$$\int_0^\infty k \, dv \int_{\theta+v}^\infty p(x)dx$$

By the further substitution

$$\theta + v = y,$$

we find

$$\int_\theta^\infty k \, dy \int_y^\infty p(x)dx = k \int_\theta^\infty p(x)dx \int_\theta^\infty dy,$$

or

$$k \int_\theta^\infty (x - \theta)p(x)dx$$

where k is determined by the condition that $P(0) = 1$, that is, $k = N$, and we recover formula (3).

The upshot of this argument is the demonstration that there are several distinct definitions of the probability that a given time interval is empty. In particular our second question can now be answered, for the probability that a time interval between θ and $\theta + d\theta$ is empty *but bounded on one side by a vehicle,* is found from the above results by taking $MB = v = 0$, while L of course precedes A. In fact, if $v = 0$ we obtain from formula (3) by differentiation

$$- \frac{dP}{d\theta} d\theta = Nd\theta \int_\theta^\infty p(x)dx$$

We shall hereafter write

$$- \frac{dP}{d\theta} = j(\theta)$$

Thus the probability that a time interval between θ and $\theta + d\theta$ is empty but bounded on one side by a vehicle is

$$-dP = j(\theta)d\theta \tag{8}$$

and the total probability of a spacing longer than θ may be written

$$\int_\theta^\infty p(x)\, dx = \frac{j(\theta)}{N} \tag{9}$$

One can also find the preceding relations in defining as follows the probability $P(\theta)$, that an interval $AB = \theta$ taken at random contains no vehicle.

Let us remark that θ being given, the random choice of AB is a process identical to that which constitutes the random choice of its origin A (or if one prefers, that of its end B).

Suppose then that one shifts along the infinite straight line an interval $AB = \theta$ and that one retains the positions of the origin A of this interval which satisfy the condition that AB contain no vehicle.

When A has been moved all along a road of total length T, the parts of the trip (on which the condition mentioned above is satisfied) will have covered a total length X $(X < T)$. It is the ratio $\frac{X}{T}$ which we consider as representing the sought-for probability $P(\theta)$ if this ratio has a fixed limit when L increased indefinitely.

Let us consider, then, two intervals of respective lengths θ and $\theta + d\theta$. At each position AB of θ there corresponds a position AB' of $\theta + d\theta$ having the same origin. If the interval AB contains some vehicles it is the same as the corresponding interval

AB'. If on the contrary, the interval θ contains nothing, what of AB' $= \theta + \mathrm{d}\,\theta$? There are only two mutually exclusive possibilities.

1. AB' contains no vehicle as is the case for AB, or
2. AB' contains one vehicle (or more) which must be on BB', if AB contains no vehicle.

If we call j(θ) dθ, the probability of this last event, we must have,

$$P(\theta) = p(\theta + \mathrm{d}\theta) + j(\theta)\mathrm{d}\theta$$

$$j(\theta) = -\frac{\mathrm{d}P(\theta)}{\mathrm{d}\theta}$$

But this last event can itself be considered as the result of two other events independent of one another:

The first one is that there is a vehicle on BB' $=$ dθ taken at random.

The second one is that the spacing before this vehicle is longer than θ.

The probability of the first event is N dθ.

The probability of the second one (when the first one has taken place) can be written

$$\int_{\theta}^{\infty} p(x)dx$$

We must have in consequence

$$j(\theta)\,\mathrm{d}\theta = N\,\mathrm{d}\theta \int_{\theta}^{\infty} p(x)\,\mathrm{d}x$$

or

$$\frac{\mathrm{d}j(\theta)}{\mathrm{d}\theta} = -Np(\theta)$$

Thus

$$p(\theta) = -\frac{\mathrm{d}j(\theta)}{\mathrm{d}\theta} \cdot \frac{1}{N} = \frac{\mathrm{d}^2\,p(\theta)}{\mathrm{d}\,\theta^{\,2}} \cdot \frac{1}{N}$$

and

$$\int_{\theta}^{\infty} p(x)\, dx = \frac{j(\theta)}{N} \tag{9}$$

is the probability that a spacing taken at random is longer than θ.

THIRD QUESTION: *Probability That an Interval x, Taken at Random, Contains Exactly n Vehicles.*

If $x_1, x_2 \ldots x_n$ are the distances from the initial point A of the interval, of various points (vehicles) $X_1, X_2 \ldots X_n$, interior to $AB = x$, (see Figure 10) we can use the preceding results to find first the probability that the first interval lying between AX_1 and $AX_1 + dx_1$, with $x_1 < x$, is empty but bounded on the right by a vehicle. This probability is $j(x_1)dx_1$.

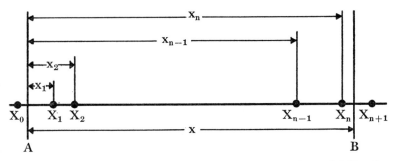

FIGURE 10. Illustration of the Third Question. $E(x,\theta)$ is the probability that $x_1, x_2 - x_1, \ldots x_n - x_{n-1}, x - x_n$ are all shorter than θ, for all the values of n greater than $\dfrac{x}{\theta}$.

Now if the point X_1 must be followed by a spacing $x_2 - x_1$, lying between $x_2 - x_1$, and $x_2 - x_1 + dx_2$, with $x_2 - x_1 < x - x_1$, we can write the probability of these two happenings:

$$j(x_1)\, dx_1\, p(x_2 - x_1)\, dx_2$$

we may continue this way up to the spacing following X_n which must be longer than $x - x_n$, and give to x_1 all the values between 0 and x, and to x_2 all the values between x_1 and x and so on up to the last interval $X_n B$ which must be shorter than the spacing between X_n and the first vehicle X_{n+1} following B. We know from (9) that the probability of this last event is $j(x - x_n)/N$.

Hence the desired probability is

$$\int_0^x j(x_1)\, dx \int_{x_1}^x p(x_2 - x_1)\, dx_2 \ldots \int_{x_{n-1}}^x p(x_n - x_{n-1})\, dx_n\, \frac{j(x - x_n)}{N} \quad (10)$$

It is this formula which gives the value

$$e^{-Nx}\, \frac{(Nx)^n}{n!} \quad \text{when} \quad P(x) = e^{-Nx}$$

FOURTH QUESTION: *Probability that for a Point Taken at Random it May be Necessary to Wait a Time x Before Finding a Gap Equal to or Greater Than θ.*

If in expression (10) above, all of the quantities x_1, $x_2 - x_1$, $\ldots$, $x_n - x_{n-1}$, $x - x_n$ remain less than a value θ given in advance, this expression gives the probability that an interval $AB = x$, placed at random in the field of the vehicles, contains n vehicles and does not contain a void of length θ or greater. These voids are intervals between A and X_1 or X_n and B. They are spacings between vehicles (gaps) in the other cases: $X_1 X_2$, $X_2 X_3$, $\ldots \ldots X_{n-1} X_n$.

If one sums all of the probabilities obtained in a similar manner, for the various possible values of n, (n an integer greater than or equal to x/θ) one obtains the probability that the interval x placed at random in the field of vehicles does not contain a void of length θ or greater.

We will designate by $E(x,\theta)$, or simply as $E(x)$ that probability which is a decreasing function of x and tends toward zero as x increases indefinitely.

Let us imagine now that $AB = x$, being placed at random in the field of vehicles, is given an increment $BB' = dx$.

There are two and only two possibilities:

1. $AB' = x + dx$ has the same properties as x
2. $AB' = x + dx$ contains a void of length θ that x does not contain.

Thus AB has at its extremity a void of length nearly equal to θ such that it lengthens dx by an amount such that the stated condition is no longer fulfilled on AB'. (See Figure 11.)

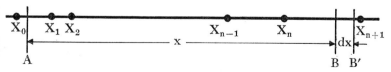

FIGURE 11. Illustration of the Fourth Question. If A B has the property stated above in Figure 10, and if A B' does not have this same property, it can be only that X_n B' (the only interval which has changed) is now equal to or greater than θ. (X_n B $< \theta \leqslant X_n$ B').

Let us call $f(x,\theta)dx$, or simply $f(x)dx$ the probability that an interval contained between x and $x + dx$ placed at random in the field of vehicles does not contain a void equal to or greater than θ *and* is bounded on the right by a vehicle.

The probability of the second event stated above can now be written:

$$f(x - \theta)\, dx\, \frac{j(\theta)}{N}$$

since the interval $x - \theta$ limited on the right by a vehicle does not allow a void equal to or greater than θ, and since the interval θ following this vehicle must itself be a void.

Thus we have:

$$E(x) = E(x + dx) + f(x - \theta)\frac{j(\theta)}{N}\, dx$$

or

$$\frac{\partial E(x)}{\partial x} = -f(x - \theta)\frac{j(\theta)}{N} \tag{11}$$

It is precisely the expression $f(x)\dfrac{j(\theta)}{N}\, dx$ that gives the probability that one point taken at random in the field of vehicles may be followed by an interval included between x and x + dx containing no gap θ or greater and terminated on a vehicle followed by a gap of θ or greater. It is thus the expression which must be evaluated to respond to the fourth question above.

We note that if $x < \theta$, $E = 1$ since in this case it is not possible to find on x a gap of θ or greater. In the same manner $f(x) = N$ since the condition to be met is reduced to that of one vehicle found between x and x + dx, which corresponds to the probability N dx.

If $x \geqslant \theta$ the stated condition requires that one vehicle less be found on the interval x. One can then separate the interval which follows the last vehicle situated on $AB = x$ and write:

$$E(x) = \int_0^\theta f(x - y) \frac{j(y)}{N} \, dy \qquad (12)$$

$$f(x) = \int_0^\theta f(x - y) \, p(y) \, dy \qquad (13)$$

For $x = \theta$ these expressions give:

$$E(\theta) = \int_0^\theta N \frac{j(y)}{N} \, dy = 1 - P(\theta), \quad \text{which we know already.}$$

$$f(\theta) = \int_0^\theta N \, p(y) \, dy = N - j(\theta)$$

Equation (13) is, furthermore, a functional expression which permits the determination of f(x) if p(y) is known between 0 and θ. Its solution will thus answer the question posed above.

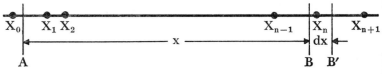

FIGURE 12.   Illustration of the Fifth Question. $f(x, \theta)dx$ is the probability that AX_1, X_1X_2, X_2X_3 . . ., $X_{n-1}X_n$, are all less than θ, for all the values of n greater than $\dfrac{x}{\theta}$ and that $x < AX_n < x + dx$.

If $X_n X_{n+1} \geqslant \theta$, AX_n is the delay one must wait before finding a gap θ following the point A. The corresponding probability is

$$f(x, \theta) \, dx \, \frac{j(\theta)}{N}$$

Fifth Question: *Probable Delay Caused by Waiting for a Gap Equal to or Greater Than θ*

The interest in the preceding considerations is the provision of a mean for calculating the probability

$$f(x) \frac{j(\theta)}{N} dx$$

of a waiting delay included between x and x + dx (See Figure 12). These considerations are not indispensable, when one calculates simply the probable waiting delay. The value is given by

$$x_m = \int_0^\infty x f(x) \frac{j(\theta)}{N} dx \tag{14}$$

which we can write according to (11)

$$x_m = - \int_0^\infty x \frac{\partial E(x + \theta)}{\partial x} dx$$

Integrating by parts

$$x_m = - [x E(x + \theta)]_0^\infty + \int_0^\infty E(x + \theta) dx$$

The first term is canceled at the two limits since E(x) tends to zero as x increases indefinitely. We have, moreover, according to (12) (since $x + \theta \geqslant \theta$)

$$E(x + \theta) = \int_0^\theta f(x + \theta - y) \frac{j(y)}{N} dy$$

x_m is therefore a double integral for which the order of integration can be reversed.

$$x_m = \int_0^\theta \frac{j(y)}{N} dy \int_0^\infty f(x + \theta - y) dy \tag{14A}$$

But by (11):

$$-f(x + \theta - y) = \frac{N}{j(\theta)} \frac{\partial E(x + 2\theta - y)}{\partial x}$$

and

$$x_m = - \int_0^\theta \frac{j(y)}{j(\theta)} \, dy \, [E(x + 2\theta - y)]_{x=0}^{x=\infty} = + \int_0^\theta \frac{j(y)}{j(\theta)} E(2\theta - y) \, dy$$

The expression for $E(2\theta - y)$ for $0 < y < \theta$ is, furthermore, easy to write since $\dfrac{\partial}{\partial y} E(2\theta - y) = f(\theta - y) \dfrac{j(\theta)}{N}$ where $\theta - y$ is contained between 0 and θ and where $f(\theta - y) = N$ as a result. We have then

$$\frac{\partial E(2\theta - y)}{\partial y} = j(\theta) \quad \text{if} \quad 0 < y < \theta$$

and, consequently

$$E(2\theta - y) = c^{te} + j(\theta)y,$$

the constant being evaluated for the condition when $y = \theta$.

$$E(\theta) = 1 - P(\theta) = C^{te} + \theta j(\theta)$$

Finally,

$$E(2\theta - y) = 1 - P(\theta) - j(\theta) (\theta - y) \quad \text{if} \quad 0 < y < \theta$$

We obtain, then, by simple calculation

$$x_m = \frac{[1 - P(\theta)]^2}{j(\theta)} - \theta \int_0^\theta P(y) dy \tag{15}$$

which is the answer to the fifth question. This outcome follows from a null wait with probability $P(\theta)$ and a probable wait.

$$X = \frac{1 - P(\theta)}{j(\theta)} - \frac{\theta - \int_0^\theta P(y) dy}{1 - P(\theta)} \tag{16}$$

with the probability $1 - P(\theta)$.

We can furthermore note that the gap θ necessary for a passing maneuver is not the same if the vehicle can overtake and pass without decreasing its speed, or if on the other hand it is constrained to wait a certain time before passing (probability $1 - P(\theta)$).

Let θ_1 and θ_2 be the gaps corresponding to these two types of passing.

It remains possible to define the function f by the equations

$$
\left.
\begin{aligned}
f(x) &= N && \text{if} && x < \theta_1 \\
f(x) &= \int_0 f(x - y)\, p(y)\, dy && \text{if} && \theta_1 \leqslant x < \theta_2 \\
f(x) &= \int_0^{\theta_2} f(x - y)\, p(y)\, dy && \text{if} && x \geqslant \theta_2
\end{aligned}
\right\} \quad (17)
$$

It is again possible to calculate, as was done above, the new value of the probable wait, but the calculations are not as straightforward. The reader will find in Appendix M the procedure which can be followed to find the probable wait in this case, from equation (14A).

But if one aims only to know this probable wait (and not the probabilities of the different values of waiting time) another more simple method can be used, which would have furnished the values given by equations (15) and (16) when $\theta_1 = \theta_2$. It consists of calculating successively the probable waits corresponding to passings impeded by a single vehicle, by two vehicles following closely, by three vehicles following closely, and so on, with partial probabilities of these different events. Thereafter there remains only the combination of the probabilities of these separate events.

If ω_1 is the probability that a first vehicle appears at a distance from the origin less than θ_1, the probability is written

$$
\omega_1 = \int_0^{\theta_1} j(x)\, dx = 1 - P(\theta_1)
$$

and the probability of being able to overtake and pass is the probability of finding after it a gap equal to or larger than θ_2. Thus the probability of passing being impeded by a single vehicle is:

$$
\pi = \omega_1 \frac{j(\theta_2)}{N}
$$

The probable distance of this single vehicle from the origin is then ξ_1 such that

$$\omega_1 \, \xi_1 = \int_0^{\theta_1} x \, j(x) \, dx = - \, \theta_1 \, P(\theta_1) + \int_0^{\theta_1} P(x) dx$$

We now denote by ω_2 the probability that a second vehicle follows the first at a distance less than θ_2. This partial probability is written

$$\omega_2 = \int_0^{\theta_2} p(x) dx = 1 - \frac{j(\theta_2)}{N}$$

The total probability that these two vehicles appear at the desired distances is then $\omega_1 \omega_2$ and the probability that one can overtake and pass after them is:

$$\pi_2 = \omega_1 \omega_2 \, \frac{j(\theta_2)}{N}$$

The probable distance of the second vehicle from the origin, X_2, is given by:

$$\pi_2 \, X_2 = \int_0^{\theta_1} dx_1 \int_0^{\theta_2} dx_2 \, (x_1 + x_2) \, j(x_1) \, p(x_2) = \omega_2 \, \xi_1 \, \omega_2 + \omega_1 \omega_2 \xi_2$$

in which

$$\omega_2 \, \xi_2 = \int_0^{\theta_2} x p(x) dx = - \, \theta_2 \, \frac{j(\theta_2)}{N} + \frac{1 - P(\theta_2)}{N}$$

It will be seen that in the same way the total probability of being prevented from overtaking and passing by k vehicles is written

$$\pi_k = \omega_1 \omega_2^{k-1} \, \frac{j(\theta_2)}{N}$$

and the probable wait corresponding to X_k is given by

$$\pi_k \, X_k = \omega_1 \xi_1 \omega_2^{k-1} \, \frac{j(\theta_2)}{N} + (k-1) \, \omega_1 \omega_2^{k-1} \xi_2 \, \frac{j(\theta_2)}{N}$$

In using the two formulas

$$\sigma_1 = 1 + x + x^2 + \ldots + x^n + \ldots = \frac{1}{1-x}$$

$$\sigma_2 = 1 + 2x + 3x^2 + \ldots + nx^{n-1} + \ldots = \frac{d\,\sigma_1}{dx} = \frac{1}{(1-x)^2}$$

we obtain successively:

1. The total probability π of one obstructed passing

$$\pi = \frac{\omega_1}{1-\omega_2} \frac{j(\theta_2)}{N} = 1 - P(\theta_1)$$

2. The corresponding wait X given by

$$\pi X = \frac{\omega_1 \xi_1}{1-\omega_2} \frac{j(\theta_2)}{N} + \frac{\omega_1 \omega_2 \xi_2}{(1-\omega_2)^2} \frac{j(\theta_2)}{N}$$

$$= \frac{[1 - P(\theta_1)] [1 - P(\theta_2)]}{j(\theta_2)} - \theta_2$$

$$+ (\theta_2 - \theta_1) P(\theta_1) + \int_0^{\theta_1} P(x)dx$$

$X_m = \pi X$ is then the resultant mean wait of the wait X with the probability $1 - P(\theta_1)$ and the null wait with the probability $P(\theta_1)$.

SIXTH QUESTION: *Mean Number of Vehicles Contained in a Group. Probability of Finding a Group With a Given Number of Vehicles.*

This question is of interest in the study of the distribution of spacings. We shall call a collection of vehicles a group if successive vehicles contained in it are separated by spacings shorter than a given value t, while successive groups are separated by spacings longer than t. Now on the basis of the preceding developments, we know that the probability of a spacing longer than t is $\frac{j(t)}{N}$, and that the probable number of spacings per unit time is therefore $j(t)$ where N is the entire number of spacings.

This is also, as we see, the probable number of groups of vehicles per unit time, and the probable mean number of vehicles in a group will be

$$\mu = \frac{N}{j(t)}$$

Moreover, the probability that there are exactly n vehicles in a group is

$$\frac{j(t)}{N} \left[1 - \frac{j(t)}{N} \right]^{n-1}$$

a result which remains valid for $n = 1$.

These considerations afford a means of determining the law of distribution of spacings (by studying the composition of the various groups of vehicles which pass a check point).

SEVENTH QUESTION: *Can one generalize the formula proposed for the case where the recordings are carried out at the exit and near to a signalized intersection?*

It is evident in this case that the large spacings have an unusually large frequency and it is perhaps necessary to adopt a probability law of the form

$$p(x) = \alpha\, p_1(x) + \beta\, p_2(x) + \gamma\, p_3(x) \qquad (\alpha + \beta + \gamma = 1)$$

in which the third term could be of the form $\gamma e^{-\frac{x}{t_3}}$ or better $\gamma e^{\frac{-x-\eta}{t_3-\eta}}$ where t_3 is a relatively large spacing and where η is the lower limit of spacings of this category.

This category of spacings corresponds in size to the interruptions of the signal light at the intersection and its importance must decrease (both γ and η decreasing) as one gets farther from the controlled intersection.

EIGHTH QUESTION: *Can two consecutive spacings be considered as independent events?*

It is this which is assumed in the preceding paragraphs and it is on this point, however, that serious doubts can be expressed.

If it is possible to construct a law of frequency distribution of spacings which represents reality, it does not mean that the order in which spacings follow each other on the route corresponds actually to random choice from this frequency law.

It is clear in the case of recordings in the vicinity of intersections controlled by automatic traffic signals, where large spacings must be interposed in a systematic fashion representing the cadence of traffic interruptions. It is incompatible with a random distribution as assumed in the preceding paragraphs.

In the general case, this systematic character must be less evident but it probably exists and corresponds to the trace of prior incidents on the route influencing the distribution of vehicles downstream.

It will then be interesting to study whether it is expedient to improve the preceding laws in diverse fashions, for example by considering the parameters α, β, γ as functions of time; or in imagining that the probability of a spacing is linked to the value thereof or a certain number of those which precede it.

The most simple hypothesis that one can make in this sense is to imagine that the presence of a spacing of one category influences the probability of the spacing which follows it immediately to belong to the same category as itself or to a different category.

If for example α is the total probability of belonging to the first category (constrained vehicles) and $\beta = 1 - \alpha$ that of belonging to the second (free vehicles), we will assume that the presence of a spacing of the first category will give the following spacing the probability $1 - \varphi\beta$ of belonging to the same category and the probability $\varphi\alpha$ of belonging to the second.

Likewise, we will assume that the presence of a spacing of the second category gives the following spacing the probability $\varphi\alpha$ of belonging to the first category and the probability $1 - \varphi\alpha$ of belonging to the second.

One can verify that the total probability that the second interval belongs to the first category is $\alpha(1 - \varphi\beta) + \beta\varphi\alpha = \alpha$ as for the first. There is not then a changing in the frequency distribution law, although the successive spacings can no longer be independent events.

One can try to reply with such a hypothesis to the questions treated above. We will limit ourselves to the case treated in the sixth question.

The mean number of platoons of vehicles remains equal to $j(z)$ and the number of vehicles per platoon to $\dfrac{N}{j(z)}$. But the mean number of isolated vehicles is equal to

$$j(z) \left[1 - \phi + \phi \frac{j(z)}{N} \right]$$

and the mean number of platoons of n vehicles $(n \geqslant 2)$ is equal to

$$\frac{j^2(z)}{N} \phi^2 \left[1 - \frac{j(z)}{N} \right] \left[1 - \phi \frac{j(z)}{N} \right]^{n-2}$$

The supplementary parameter which φ constitutes evidently permits a better adaptation of these formulas to measurements carried out on the route. But it remains of course to know if this new parameter corresponds well to physical reality and if its use has a good effect of restraining the part due to chance in the distribution law. Only systematic trials on the manner of spacing succession will permit response to this question.

CONCLUSION

It appears that the results presented in this chapter can lead to a considerably closer agreement between theory and observation than has been obtained heretofore. Their interest lies in the fact that in spite of the somewhat complicated form of the law we have chosen for the probability of spacings between successive vehicles, the values which it gives in answer to our six fundamental questions are comparatively simple. They involve only the functions P, j, and p. Of course one could, if one preferred, start with a purely empirical law, as for example the empirical curve of Figure 7 which is simply $\dfrac{j(\theta)}{N}$, and from this obtain the curves for P and p by graphical integration or differentiation. Our questions could thus be answered without any assumed law of probability.

It is hoped that these results will be useful to those interested in traffic research, who recognize the growing importance of statistical studies in this field. They may also throw light on certain extensions of Poisson's Law.

APPENDIX A

Greek Alphabet

Name	Lower Case	Upper Case
Alpha	α	A
Beta	β	B
Gamma	γ	Γ
Delta	δ	Δ
Epsilon	ε	E
Zeta	ζ	Z
Eta	η	H
Theta	θ	Θ
Iota	ι	I
Kappa	ϰ	K
Lambda	λ	Λ
Mu	μ	M
Nu	ν	N
Xi	ξ	Ξ
Omicron	o	O
Pi	π	Π
Rho	ρ	P
Sigma	σ	Σ
Tau	τ	T
Upsilon	υ	Υ
Phi	φ	Φ
Chi	χ	X
Psi	ψ	Ψ
Omega	ω	Ω

APPENDIX B

Permutations and Combinations

The subject of permutations may be easily illustrated by the example of code words. Consider that 3 cards marked A, B, C are available and are to be used to form as many 3-letter code words as possible. The result will be:

$$A\Big\langle\begin{matrix}B\ C\\C\ B\end{matrix} \qquad\qquad \begin{matrix}A\ B\ C\\A\ C\ B\end{matrix}$$

$$B\Big\langle\begin{matrix}A\ C\\C\ A\end{matrix} \qquad\qquad \begin{matrix}B\ A\ C\\B\ C\ A\end{matrix}$$

$$C\Big\langle\begin{matrix}A\ B\\B\ A\end{matrix} \qquad\qquad \begin{matrix}C\ A\ B\\C\ B\ A\end{matrix}$$

In each case there will be 3 choices for the first letter, 2 choices for the second letter, and 1 choice for the third letter. From this it follows that:

P_n^n = Permutations of n things taken n at a time

$\quad = n\ (n - 1)\ (n - 2)\ldots 3 \cdot 2 \cdot 1$

$\quad = n! = $ factorial n

$P_3^3 = 3 \cdot 2 \cdot 1 = 6$ which checks the empirical result

If there are 5 cards marked A, B, C, D, E and it is desired that 3-letter code words be formed, there will be 5 choices for the first letter, 4 choices for the second, and 3 for the third:

$$P_3^5 = \text{Permutations of 5 things taken 3 at a time}$$

$$= 5 \cdot 4 \cdot 3 = 60$$

$$= \frac{5 \cdot 4 \cdot 3 \cdot 2 \cdot 1}{2 \cdot 1} = \frac{5!}{2!} = \frac{5!}{(5-3)!}$$

For the general case of the permutations of n things taken m at a time

$$P_m^n = \frac{n!}{(n-m)!}$$

In these code words the order is important, for ABC is a different *permutation* from ACB. Consider, however, 3-card hands formed from the 5 cards A, K, Q, J, 10. If order were important, there would be 60 permutations as follows:

AKQ AQJ AJ10 KQJ AKJ AK10 AQ10 KJ10 KQ10 QJ10

AQK AJQ A10J KJQ AJK A10K A10Q K10J K10Q Q10J

KAQ QAJ JA10 QKJ KAJ KA10 QA10 JK10 QK10 JQ10

KQA QJA J10A QJK KJA K10A Q10A J10K Q10K J10Q

QAK JAQ 10AJ JKQ JAK 10AK 10AQ 10KJ 10KQ 10QJ

QKA JQA 10JA JQK JKA 10KA 10QA 10JK 10QK 10JQ

Note that each vertical group is P_3^3 while the whole array is P_3^5. In general, however, the order of the cards is unimportant. It is the particular group of cards that is important (represented by the 10 groups above). When order is unimportant the grouping is known as a *combination*.

$$C_3^5 = \frac{\text{Combinations of 5 things taken 3 at a time}}{} = \frac{\text{Permut. of whole array}}{\text{Permut. within combination}}$$

$$= \frac{P_3^5}{P_3^3} = \frac{60}{6} = 10$$

$$C_m^n = \frac{P_m^n}{P_m^m} = \frac{n!}{(n-m)!\, m!}$$

Factorial Zero

For clarity in certain problems it has been found convenient to define the factorial zero as follows:

$$(n - 1)! = \frac{n!}{n}$$

let:

$$n = 1$$

then:

$$(1 - 1)! = \frac{1!}{1}$$

$$0! = 1$$

Laws of Probability

The following are two important laws concerning probability:

1. Total Probability

   If two events, A and B, are mutually exclusive (if A occurs, B cannot occur and vice versa) the total probability that one of these events will occur is:

   $$P(A \text{ or } B) = P(A + B) = P(A) + P(B) \leqslant 1$$

2. Joint Probability

   If two events, A and B, are independent (the occurrence of one has no influence on the other) the probability that both will occur together is:

   $$P(AB) = P(A \text{ and } B) = P(A)P(B)$$

APPENDIX C

The Binomial Distribution

Consider a population in which each item may possess one of two mutually exclusive characteristics (head or tail, good or bad, 0 or 1, etc.).

Let: p = probability of occurrence of characteristic A

$q = (1 - p)$ = probability of occurrence of characteristic B

(non-occurrence of A)

Then, by the law of total probability,

$$P(A \text{ or } B) = p + q$$

Suppose that a sample of n items is drawn from the population under the following conditions:

a. The size of the population is infinite. (This restriction insures that withdrawing the sample does not alter the relative proportion of A and B remaining in the population. The same result may be achieved with a finite population by drawing one item, replacing, stirring, drawing the next item, etc.)

b. The sample is selected from the population at random.

Then, by the law of joint probability:
the probability that all n items in the sample
  are A's = p^n
the probability of $(n - 1)$ A's and 1 B = $p^{n-1} q$ where the order of
the probability of $(n - 2)$ A's and 2 B's = $p^{n-2} q^2$ A's and
  etc.   B's is
the probability of 1A and $(n - 1)$ B's = pq^{n-1} significant
the probability of n B's = q^n

In general, for m A's and $(n - m)$ B's the probability = $p^m q^{n-m}$

where $m = 0, 1, 2, \ldots (n - 1), n$

In drawing the sample, the order in which the A's occur can take on many possibilities, the number being equal to the combinations of n things taken m at a time $= C^n_m$
For instance, if the number of items in the sample is 5, there are $C^5_3 = 10$ ways in which a sample composed of 3 A's and 2 B's may be drawn. Each of these ways will have a probability of p^3q^2. Thus, by the law of total probability, the probability of 3 A's and 2 B's is:

$$10p^3q^2$$

or in general:

$$C^n_m p^m q^{n-m}$$

Considering the various possibilities of 0, 1, 2, ... n A's and n, (n − 1) .... 1, 0 B's, the total probability of occurrence of A's and B's is given by

$$P(A, B) = \sum_{m=0}^{n} C^n_m p^m q^{n-m}$$

The right hand member is equal to $(q + p)^n$ and hence this relationship is known as the binomial distribution.

$$\sum_{m=0}^{n} C^n_m p^m q^{n-m} = (p + q)^n$$

APPENDIX D

The Poisson Distribution is applicable to populations having the following properties:

a. The probability of occurrence of individuals having a particular characteristic is low.
b. The characteristic is a discrete variable.

The Poisson distribution can be derived as a limiting case of the binomial distribution. (This is the most commonly seen derivation.) It is possible, however, to derive the Poisson distribution directly from fundamental considerations of probability.

The Poisson Distribution as a Limiting Case of the Binomial Distribution

Let n = number of items in sample
p = probability of occurrence of a particular characteristic E
q = (1 − p) = probability of non-occurrence of characteristic E
x = number of items in sample having characteristic E.

Then, from the binomial distribution:

$$P(x) = C_x^n p^x q^{n-x} = C_x^n p^x (1 - p)^{n-x}$$

$$x = 0, 1, 2, \ldots . n$$

Now let:

p be made indefinitely small

n be very large

pn = m, where m is finite and not necessarily small.

Then:

$$p = \frac{m}{n}$$

$$P(x) = C_x^n \left(\frac{m}{n}\right)^x \left(1 - \frac{m}{n}\right)^{n-x}; \quad x = 0, 1, 2, \ldots n$$

$$= \frac{n!}{x!\,(n-x)!} \left(\frac{m}{n}\right)^x \left(1 - \frac{m}{n}\right)^{n-x}$$

$$= \frac{n!}{x!\,(n-x)!} \left(\frac{m}{n}\right)^x \left(1 - \frac{m}{n}\right)^n \left(1 - \frac{m}{n}\right)^{-x}$$

$$P(x) = \left[\frac{m^x}{x!}\right] \left[\left(1 - \frac{m}{n}\right)^n\right] \left[\frac{n!}{(n-x)!\,n^x \left(1 - \frac{m}{n}\right)^x}\right]$$

$$= [A][B][C]$$

where A, B, and C represent the individual terms in brackets.
Now, if $n \to \infty$

$$\lim_{n \to \infty} P(x) = \lim_{n \to \infty} \left\{[A][B][C]\right\}$$

$$= \left[\lim_{n \to \infty} A\right]\left[\lim_{n \to \infty} B\right]\left[\lim_{n \to \infty} C\right]$$

$$A = \frac{m^x}{x!}$$

$$\lim_{n \to \infty} A = \frac{m^x}{x!}$$

$$B = \left(1 - \frac{m}{n}\right)^n$$

$$\lim_{n \to \infty} B = e^{-m} \qquad \text{(See Appendix E for proof)}$$

$$C = \frac{n!}{(n-x)!\,n^x \left(1 - \frac{m}{n}\right)^x}$$

When n is very large, negligible error is introduced by representing n! by one term of Stirling's formula. The same statement holds for (n — x)!

Therefore,

$$C = \frac{\sqrt{2\pi n}\ \ n^n\ e^{-n}}{\sqrt{2\pi(n-x)}\ (n-x)^{n-x}\ e^{-(n-x)}\left(1-\dfrac{m}{n}\right)^x n^x}$$

$$C = \frac{\sqrt{2\pi}\ \ n^{\frac{1}{2}}\ e^{-n}\ n^n}{\sqrt{2\pi}\ (n-x)^{\frac{1}{2}}\ (n-x)^{n-x}\ e^{-(n-x)}\left(1-\dfrac{m}{n}\right)^x n^x}$$

$$= e^{-x}\left(\frac{n-x}{n}\right)^{-\frac{1}{2}}\frac{n^{n-x}}{(n-x)^{n-x}}\frac{1}{\left(1-\dfrac{m}{n}\right)^x}$$

$$= e^{-x}\left(1-\frac{x}{n}\right)^{-\frac{1}{2}}\frac{1}{\left(\dfrac{n-x}{n}\right)^{n-x}}\frac{1}{\left(1-\dfrac{m}{n}\right)^x}$$

$$C = [e^{-x}]\left[1-\frac{x}{n}\right]^{-\frac{1}{2}}\frac{1}{\left(1-\dfrac{x}{n}\right)^{n-x}}\frac{1}{\left(1-\dfrac{m}{n}\right)^x}$$

$$= [e^{-x}]\left[1-\frac{x}{n}\right]^{x-\frac{1}{2}}\left[\frac{1}{\left(1-\dfrac{x}{n}\right)^{n}}\right]\left[\frac{1}{\left(1-\dfrac{m}{n}\right)^x}\right]$$

$$= [C_1][C_2][C_3][C_4]$$

where C_1, C_2, C_3, and C_4 represent the individual terms in brackets

$$C_1 = e^{-x}$$

$$\lim_{n\to\infty} C_1 = e^{-x}$$

$$C_2 = \left(1-\frac{x}{n}\right)^{x-\frac{1}{2}}$$

$$\lim_{n \to \infty} C_2 = 1$$

$$C_3 = \frac{1}{\left(1 - \dfrac{x}{n}\right)^n}$$

$$\lim_{n \to \infty} C_3 = \frac{1}{e^{-x}}$$
   (See Appendix E)

$$C_4 = \frac{1}{\left(1 - \dfrac{m}{n}\right)^x}$$

$$\lim_{n \to \infty} C_4 = 1$$

$$\lim_{n \to \infty} C = \left[\lim_{n \to \infty} C_1\right]\left[\lim_{n \to \infty} C_2\right]\left[\lim_{n \to \infty} C_3\right]\left[\lim_{n \to \infty} C_4\right]$$

$$= [e^{-x}]\,[1]\left[\frac{1}{e^{-x}}\right][1]$$

$$= 1$$

$$\lim_{n \to \infty} P(x) = \frac{m^x}{x!}\,e^{-m}$$

Since the main body of this discussion assumes the existence of the conditions for the Poisson distribution, (i.e., $n \to \infty$) the above equation may be written simply:

$$P(x) = \frac{m^x}{x!}\,e^{-m}$$

Direct Derivation of the Poisson Distribution (1, 2, 3)

Consider a process in which the average or expected rate of arrival is λ arrivals per unit time.

Let

$P_i(t) =$ the probability of i arrivals up to the time t.
$\lambda dt =$ the probability of one arrival in the incremental period dt.

Note: It is assumed that dt is of such a short duration that the probability of more than one arrival in dt is negligible

$$\therefore (1 - \lambda dt) = \text{the probability of no arrival in dt.}$$

Then:

$P_i(t + dt)$ = the probability that i arrivals have taken place up to the time $(t + dt)$

= [Prob $(i - 1$ arrivals in t) · Prob (1 arrival in dt)]

+ [Prob (i arrivals in t) · Prob (0 arrivals in dt)]

$$P_i(t + dt) = P_{i-1}(t) \cdot P_1(dt) + P_i(t) \cdot P_0(dt)$$

$$= P_{i-1}(t) \lambda dt + P_i(t) (1 - \lambda dt)$$

$$= [P_{i-1}(t) - P_i(t)] (\lambda dt) + P_i(t)$$

$$\frac{P_i(t + dt) - P_i(t)}{dt} = \lambda [P_{i-1}(t) - P_i(t)]$$

or

$$\frac{dP_i(t)}{dt} = \lambda [P_{i-1}(t) - P_i(t)] \qquad\qquad [\text{A}$$

Now,

$$P_{-1}(t) = 0 \qquad\qquad \text{(i.e., impossible to have less than zero)}$$

$$P_0(0) = 1 \qquad\qquad \text{(i.e., no arrivals up to time } t = 0)$$

$$P_i(0) = 0 \quad \text{for } i \geqslant 1 \text{ (zero probability of i arrivals at time } t = 0$$

Setting i = 0 in Equation [A]

$$\frac{dP_0(t)}{dt} = \lambda [0 - P_0(t)]$$

$$\frac{dP_0(t)}{P_0(t)} = -\lambda dt$$

$$\ln P_0(t) = -\lambda t + c$$

$$P_0(t) = e^{-\lambda t + c}$$

Since

$$P_0(0) = 1$$

and

$$1 = e^0$$

$$\therefore c = 0$$

and

$$P_0(t) = e^{-\lambda t}$$

Setting $i = 1$ in Equation [A] and inserting the above value for $P_0(t)$

$$\frac{dP_1(t)}{dt} = \lambda[e^{-\lambda t} - P_1(t)]$$

$$\frac{dP_1(t)}{dt} + \lambda P_1(t) = \lambda e^{-\lambda t}$$

Using method of operators for solving this differential equation*

$$(D + \lambda)\,P_1(t) = \lambda\,e^{-\lambda t}$$

$$P_1(t) = \frac{1}{D + \lambda}\,\lambda\,e^{-\lambda t}$$

$$= (\lambda t)\,e^{-\lambda t} + C_2\,e^{-\lambda t}$$

But

$$P_1(0) = 0;\;\therefore C_2 = 0$$

$$\therefore P_1(t) = (\lambda t)\,e^{-\lambda t}$$

$$\frac{dP_2(t)}{dt} = \lambda\,[P_1(t) - P_2(t)]$$

$$\frac{dP_2(t)}{dt} + \lambda\,P_2(t) = \lambda\,P_1(t) = \lambda\,(\lambda t)\,e^{-\lambda t}$$

$$P_2(t) = \frac{1}{D + \lambda}\,\lambda\,(\lambda t)\,e^{-\lambda t}$$

* Any standard method may be used for solution of this differential equation.
The method of operators is particularly simple. See any standard text, such as
ord (4). The form

$$y = \frac{1}{D + A}u(x)$$

sults in a solution

$$y = e^{-Ax}\int e^{Ax}u(x)dx + c\,e^{-Ax}$$

$$= \frac{\lambda^2 t^2}{2} e^{-\lambda t} + C_3 e^{-\lambda t}$$

But
$$P_2(0) = 0 \qquad \therefore C_3 = 0$$

$$P_2(t) = \frac{(\lambda t)^2 e^{-\lambda t}}{2}$$

Similarly,

$$P_3(t) = \frac{(\lambda t)^3 e^{-\lambda t}}{3!}$$

$$P_4(t) = \frac{(\lambda t)^4 e^{-\lambda t}}{4!}$$

$$P_x(t) = \frac{(\lambda t)^x e^{-\lambda t}}{x!}$$

This is the form of the Poisson distribution used at the end of Chapter II. If λt is set equal to m, the result is the form of the Poisson distribution used in the balance of Chapter II as well as in Chapter I.

REFERENCES FOR APPENDIX D

1. Feller, William, *An Introduction to Probability and Its Applications*, Vol. 1, First edition, Wiley, 1950, pp. 364–367.
2. Arley, Niels, and Buch, K. R., *Introduction to the Theory of Probability and Statistics*, Wiley, 1950, pp. 30–31.
3. Fry, Thornton C., *Probability and Its Engineering Uses*, Van Nostrand, 1928, pp. 220–227.
4. Ford, L. R., *Differential Equations*, McGraw-Hill, 1933, p. 172.

APPENDIX E

DERIVATION OF LIMIT $\lim_{n \to \infty} \left(1 - \dfrac{m}{n}\right)^n$ **(USED IN THE DERIVATION OF THE POISSON DISTRIBUTION)**

$$\text{Let } n = \frac{1}{x}$$

$$\lim_{n \to \infty} \left(1 - \frac{m}{n}\right)^n = \lim_{\frac{1}{x} \to \infty} (1 - mx)^{\frac{1}{x}}; \text{ where } n = \frac{1}{x}$$

$$= \lim_{\frac{1}{x} \to \infty} \left[1 - \left(\frac{1}{x}\right)(mx) + \frac{\left(\frac{1}{x}\right)\left(\frac{1}{x} - 1\right)(mx)^2}{2!} \right.$$

$$\left. - \frac{\left(\frac{1}{x}\right)\left(\frac{1}{x} - 1\right)\left(\frac{1}{x} - 2\right)(mx)^3}{3!} + \cdots \right]$$

$$= \lim_{\frac{1}{x} \to \infty} \left[1 - m + \frac{m^2}{2!}(1 - x) - \frac{m^3}{3!}(1 - x)(1 - 2x) + \cdots \right]$$

$$= 1 - m + \frac{m^2}{2!} - \frac{m^3}{3!} + \cdots$$

But expanding e^{-m} in a McLaurin series gives:

$$e^{-m} = 1 - m + \frac{m^2}{2!} - \frac{m^3}{3!} + \cdots$$

Therefore

$$\lim_{n \to \infty} \left(1 - \frac{m}{n}\right)^n = e^{-m}$$

APPENDIX F

Sample Statistics

The sample mean, $\bar{x}$, of a group of observations is computed

$$\bar{x} = \frac{1}{n} \sum_{i=0}^{n} x_i$$

In fitting a Poisson distribution to observed data, $\bar{x}$ is used as an estimate of the Poisson parameter m.

An important statistic of observed data is the variance s^2.[*] The computation of the variance is most conveniently carried out

$$s^2 = \frac{\sum_{i=1}^{n} f_i x_i^2 - \dfrac{\left(\sum_{i=1}^{n} f_i x_i\right)^2}{n}}{n-1}$$

where f_i is the frequency of occurrence of event x_i.

Mean, Variance, and Standard Deviation of Poisson Distribution

1. Mean

The mean of a continuous function is obtained by:

---

[*] Most correctly, s^2 is an unbiased estimate of the population variance based on the sample. The $(n-1)$ in the denominator is necessary to make this an unbiased estimate. For an excellent explanation of this correction (known as Bessel's correction) see the account on pp. 289–290 of Neville and Kennedy (1).

112

$$\mu = \frac{\int xf(x)dx}{\int f(x)dx}$$

(The mean may be considered as the distance to the center of gravity.) For discrete functions the comparable function defining the mean is:

$$\mu = \frac{\Sigma xf(x)}{\Sigma f(x)}$$

When dealing with probabilities:

$$\Sigma f(x) = n$$

$$\frac{f(x)}{n_i} = P(x)$$

$$\sum_{x=0}^{\infty} P(x) = 1$$

Thus
$$\mu = \int xP(x)$$

or

$$\mu = \sum_{x=0}^{\infty} x\,P(x)$$

For the Poisson distribution

$$P(x) = \frac{m^x e^{-m}}{m!}$$

$$\mu = \sum_{x=0}^{\infty} \frac{xm^x e^{-m}}{m!}$$

$$= 0 + me^{-m} + \frac{2m^2 e^{-m}}{2!} + \frac{3m^2 e^{-m}}{3!}$$

$$= me^{-m}\left[1 + m + \frac{m^2}{2!} + \frac{m^3}{3!} \ldots \right]$$

$$= me^{-m}e^m$$

$$= m$$

2. Variance

By definition, the variance σ^2 may be expressed:

$$\sigma^2 = \frac{\Sigma f(x)\ (x - \mu)^2}{\Sigma f(x)}$$

For the Poisson distribution

$$\sigma^2 = \frac{\Sigma(x - m)^2\ f(x)}{\Sigma f(x)} = \frac{\Sigma(x^2 - 2xm + m^2)\ P(x)}{1}$$

$$= \Sigma x^2 P(x) - 2m\Sigma x P(x) + m^2\Sigma P(x)$$

The last two terms reduce as follows:

$$-2m\Sigma x P(x) = -2m(m) = -2m^2$$

$$m^2\Sigma P(x) = m^2$$

The first term may be reduced by the following steps:

$$\Sigma x^2 P(x) = \Sigma[x(x - 1) + x]\ P(x) = \Sigma x(x - 1)\ P(x) + \Sigma x P(x)$$

$$= \Sigma x(x - 1)\ P(x) + m$$

$$= \left[0 + 0 + \frac{2m^2\ e^{-m}}{2!} + \frac{6m^3\ e^{-m}}{3!} + \frac{12m^4\ e^{-m}}{4!} + \ldots \right] + m$$

$$= m^2\ e^{-m} \left(1 + m + \frac{m^2}{2!} + \ldots \right) + m$$

$$= m^2\ e^{-m}(e^m) + m = m^2 + m$$

$$\sigma^2 = m^2 + m - 2m^2 + m^2 = m$$

3. Standard Deviation

By definition the standard deviation, σ, is expressed by

$$\sigma = \sqrt{\sigma^2}$$

Thus, for the Poisson distribution

$$\sigma = \sqrt{m}$$

Summary for Other Distributions

Expressions for the mean and variance of other distributions are shown in the summary table below.

SUMMARY OF EXPRESSIONS FOR MEAN AND VARIANCE

Distribution	Mean	Variance
Poisson	m	m
Binomial	np	$np(1 - p)$
Negative Binomial	$k(1 - p)/p$	$k(1 - p)/p^2$
Exponential	T	T^2
Erlang	T	T^2/k

REFERENCE FOR APPENDIX F

1. Neville, Adam M., and Kennedy, John B., *Basic Statistical Methods for Engineers and Scientists*, International Textbook Co., 1964.

APPENDIX G

Let: f = Observed frequency for any group or interval

F = Computed or theoretical frequency for same group

Then, by definition:

$$\chi^2 = \sum_{i=1}^{g} \frac{(f_i - F_i)^2}{F_i} \qquad (1)$$

where g = number of groups

Expanding:

$$\chi^2 = \sum_{i=1}^{g} \left[\frac{f_i^2}{F_i} - \frac{2f_iF_i}{F_i} + \frac{F_i^2}{F_i} \right]$$

$$= \sum_{i=1}^{g} \frac{f_i^2}{F_i} - 2 \sum_{i=1}^{g} f_i + \sum_{i=1}^{g} F_i$$

But by assumption in the fitting process:

$$\sum_{i=1}^{g} f_i = \sum_{i=1}^{g} F_i = n$$

where n = total number of observations

So that:

$$\chi^2 = \left(\sum_{i=1}^{g} \frac{f_i^2}{F_i} \right) - n \qquad (2)$$

Either equation (1) or equation (2) may be used for purposes of computation. Usually (2) will simplify the amount of work involved. (See Example 8.)

116

The value of χ^2 obtained as above is then compared with the value from Figure G1 or from tables of χ^2. Such tables may be found in any collection of statistical tables, and relate the values of χ^2 and significance level with the degrees of freedom. The number of degrees of freedom, v, may be expressed: (1, 2, 3)

$$v = (g - 1) - A$$

where g = number of groups

A = number of parameters estimated in the fitting process

The following table lists information for several distributions

Distribution	A	v
Poisson	1	$g - 2$
Negative Binomial	2	$g - 3$
Generalized Poisson	2	$g - 3$
Binomial	2	$g - 3$

For this value of v to be valid, however, it is necessary that the theoretical number of occurrences in any group be at least 5. One writer (3) further stipulates that the total number of observations be at least 50. When the number of theoretical occurrences in any group is less than 5, the group interval should be increased. For the lowest and highest groups this may be accomplished by making these groups "all less than" and "all greater than", respectively. (See the discussion preceding and the footnote following Example 7. Also see Example 8.)

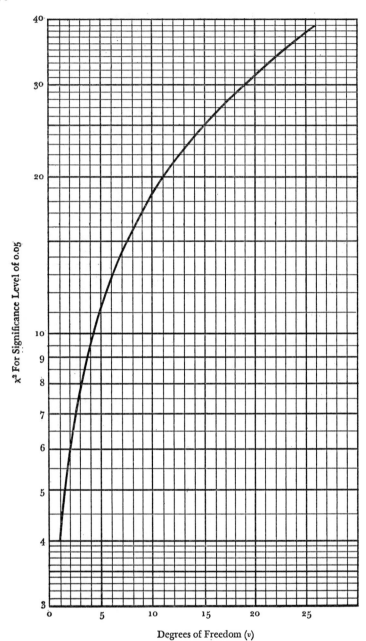

FIGURE G-1.   Values of χ^2

REFERENCES FOR APPENDIX G

1. Dixon, Wilfred J., and Massey, Frank J., Jr., *Introduction to Statistical Analysis*, McGraw-Hill, 1957, pp. 226–227.
2. Yule, G. Udny, and Kendall, M. G., *An Introduction to the Theory of Statistics*, 14th edition, Haffner Publishing Company, 1950, p. 475, p. 477.
3. Cramer, Harald, *Mathematical Methods of Statistics*, Princeton University Press, 1946, p. 435.

APPENDIX H

The Kolmogorov-Smirnov Test for Goodness of Fit

The Kolmogorov-Smirnov (K-S) Test for Goodness of Fit may be used in lieu of the more familiar χ^2 test in many instances. Like the χ^2 test it is non-parametric, i.e., no assumptions are made concerning the populations under consideration. An excellent discussion of the K-S test is given by Massey (1).

The test is based on the simple measurement of the maximum vertical difference between the two cumulative distributions, i.e., the observed cumulative probability distribution and the theoretical cumulative probability distribution.* This difference, d, is then compared with the value of the K-S statistic for the appropriate sample size and level of significance. An abbreviated table of the K-S statistic d is shown in Table H1.

As noted by Walker and Lev (2), in comparing the K-S and χ^2 tests, the K-S test requires much less computation and is applicable to smaller samples. It is also noted that, where applicable, the K-S test is believed to be more sensitive than the χ^2 test.

There is a restriction, however, that the K-S test may not be used where the population parameters are estimated from the same sample as that whose fit is being tested.

* Most properly, the "observed" distribution is the cumulative *relative* frequency.

TABLE H1

Values of the Kolmogorov-Smirnov Test Statistic "d", the Maximum Vertical Difference between two cumulative distributions, for various sample sizes and levels of significance (after Massey *(1)*).

Sample Size (N)	Level of Significance (α)		
	0.10	*0.05*	*0.01*
1	0.950	0.975	0.995
2	0.776	0.842	0.929
3	0.642	0.708	0.828
4	0.564	0.624	0.733
5	0.510	0.565	0.669
6	0.470	0.521	0.618
7	0.438	0.486	0.577
8	0.411	0.457	0.543
9	0.388	0.432	0.514
10	0.368	0.410	0.490
11	0.352	0.391	0.468
12	0.338	0.375	0.450
13	0.325	0.361	0.433
14	0.314	0.349	0.418
15	0.304	0.338	0.404
16	0.295	0.328	0.392
17	0.286	0.318	0.381
18	0.278	0.309	0.371
19	0.272	0.301	0.363
20	0.264	0.294	0.356
25	0.24	0.27	0.32
30	0.22	0.24	0.29
35	0.21	0.23	0.27
>35	$\dfrac{1.22}{\sqrt{N}}$	$\dfrac{1.36}{\sqrt{N}}$	$\dfrac{1.63}{\sqrt{N}}$

REFERENCES FOR APPENDIX H

1. Massey, Frank J., Jr., "The Kolmogorov-Smirnov Test for Goodness of Fit," *Journal of the American Statistical Association,* Vol. 46, 1951, pp. 68–78.
2. Walker, Helen M., and Lev, Joseph, *Statistical Inference,* Henry Holt and Co., New York, 1953, p. 443.

APPENDIX I

DERIVATION OF THE DISTRIBUTION OF THE SUM OF INDEPENDENT POISSON DISTRIBUTIONS

Consider a population made up of two subpopulations A and B, each distributed according to the Poisson distribution.
For subpopulation A

$$P(x_a) = \frac{m_a^{x_a} e^{-m_a}}{x_a!}$$

For subpopulation B

$$P(x_b) = \frac{m_a^{x_b} e^{-m_b}}{x_b!}$$

If k items occur in a trial from the total population, there may be a mixture of x_a and x_b as follows:

$x_a = k;$	$x_b = 0$	$x_a + x_b = k$
$x_a = k - 1$	$x_b = 1$	$x_a + x_b = k$
$x_a = k - 2$	$x_b = 2$	$x_a + x_b = k$
. . . . . .		
$x_a = 2$	$x_b = k - 2$	$x_a + x_b = k$
$x_a = 1$	$x_b = k - 1$	$x_a + x_b = k$
$x_a = 0$	$x_b = k$	$x_a + x_b = k$

$$P(k) = P(x_a = k, x_b = 0) + P(x_a = k - 1, x_b = 1) \ldots\ldots$$

$$+ P(x_a = 1, x_b = k - 1) + P(x_a = 0, x_b = k)$$

$$= \frac{m_a^k e^{-m_a} e^{-m_b}}{k!\, 0!} + \frac{m_a^{k-1} e^{-m_a} m_b\, e^{-m_b}}{(k-1)!\, 1!} + \frac{m_a^{k-2} e^{-m_a} m_b^2\, e^{-m_b}}{(k-2)!\, 2!}$$

$$+ \ldots \ldots + \frac{m_a e^{-m_a} m_b^{k-1} e^{-m_b}}{1! (k-1)!} + \frac{e^{-m_a} m_b^k e^{-m_b}}{0! \, k!}$$

$$P(k) = e^{-m_a} e^{-m_b} \left\{ \frac{m_a^k}{k!} + \frac{k m_a^{k-1} m_b}{k(k-1)!} + \frac{k(k-1) m_a^{k-2} m_b^2}{k(k-1)(k-2)! \, 2!} \right.$$

$$\left. + \ldots \ldots + \frac{k(k-1) \ldots 3 \cdot 2 \cdot 1 \, m_a m_b^{k-1}}{k(k-1) \ldots 3 \cdot 2 \cdot 1 \, (k-1)!} + \frac{m_b^k}{k!} \right\}$$

$$P(k) = \frac{e^{-(m_a+m_b)}}{k!} \left\{ m_a^k + k m_a^{k-1} m_b + \frac{k(k-1) m^{k-2} m_b^2}{2!} \right.$$

$$\left. + \ldots + k m_a m_b^{k-1} + m_b^k \right\}$$

$$P(k) = \frac{e^{-(m_a+m_b)} (m_a + m_b)^k}{k!}$$

When there are subpopulations A, B, ... , Z, by application of a similar argument the distribution for the whole population is found to be

$$P(k) = \frac{(m_a + m_b + \ldots + m_z)^k \, e^{-(m_a+m_b+\ldots+m_z)}}{k!}$$

APPENDIX J

COMPUTER PROGRAM FOR SELECTING AND FITTING A COUNTING DISTRIBUTION*

```
      PROGRAM PRODIS  (INPUT, OUTPUT, TAPE5=INPUT, TAPE6=OUTPUT)
C     THIS PROBABILITY DISTRIBUTION PROGRAM (PRODIS) ACCEPTS FIELD DATA
C     IN THE FORM OF COUNTS AND, AFTER COMPUTING THE MEAN AND VARIANCE,
C     FITS THE APPROPRIATE COUNTING DISTRIBUTION TO THE DATA. THE OUTPUT
C     ITEMS ARE APPROPRIATELY IDENTIFIED. THE INPUT DATA MUST BE PUNCHED
C     ONE OBSERVATION PER CARD IN THE FORM XXYYYY IN COLUMNS 1 TO 6,
C     WHERE XX (IN COLUMNS 1, 2) IS THE EVENT, AND YYYY (COLUMNS 3 TO 6)
C     IS THE FREQUENCY WITH WHICH THIS EVENT IS OBSERVED. AFTER EACH
C     SET OF DATA (E.G. EACH STATION OR PERIOD OF OBSERVATION) A CARD WITH
C     NEGATIVE FREQUENCY (E.G. 00-999) SHOULD BE INSERTED.
C     THE FOLLOWING EXAMPLE ILLUSTRATES THE CORRESPONDENCE BETWEEN CARD
C     PUNCHING AND OBSERVED DATA. EACH DATA SET SHOULD BE PRECEDED BY
C     A HEADING CARD GIVING THE RUN IDENTIFICATION ETC.
C
C     EVENT    FREQUENCY    CARD PUNCHING      REMARKS
C                          (COLUMNS 1 TO 6)
C
C     HIGHWAY 23 AT ELM NORTHBOUND          (HEADING CARD)
C        0         0           000000
C        1         0           010000
C        2         0           020000
C        3         3           030003
C        4         0           040000
C        5         8           050008
C        6        10           060010
C        7        11           070011
C        8        10           080010
C        9        11           090011
C       10         9           100009
C       11         1           110001
C       12         1           120001
C     END        ---          00-999     END OF DATA SET 1.
C
C     MAIN STREET-RUN 23                    (HEADING CARD)
C        0       139           000139
C        1       128           010128
C        2        55           020055
C        3        25           030025
C        4        10           040010
C        5         3           050003
C     END        ---          00-999     END OF DATA SET 2.
C
      DIMENSION FRQ(90),THP(90),THB(90),PKS(90),BKS(90),P(90),T(200)
      DIMENSION           HEAD(10), CMR(90), CMP(90), CMB(90),B(90),REL(90)
      DIMENSION DELT(90)
      REAL MEAN
      INTEGER X, XL
   10 XL = 0
      SUMX = 0
      SUMSQ = 0
      TOTAL = 0
C
C     **********READ DATA AND COMPUTE MEAN, VARIANCE, AND RATIO****
C
      DO 50       I=1, 90
   50 FRQ(I) = 0
      READ (5,170) ( HEAD(I), I = 1, 10)
```

* Written by D. L. Gerlough, 1969.

```
      IF (EOF, 5) 1700, 70                                              057
   70 WRITE (6,172) ( HEAD(I), I = 1, 10)                               058
   75 READ (5, 171) X, FR                                              059
   90 IF (FR.LT.0.0) GO TO 150                                         060
      I = X + 1                                                        061
      IF (X - XL) 101, 101, 100                                        062
  100 XL = X                                                           063
      IW = XL + 3                                                      064
  101 FRQ(I) = FR                                                      065
  140 SUMX = SUMX + FR*X                                               066
      SUMSQ = SUMSQ + FR*X**2                                          067
      TOTAL = TOTAL + FR                                               068
      GO TO 75                                                         069
  150 MEAN = SUMX/TOTAL                                                070
      VAR = (SUMSQ - (SUMX**2)/TOTAL)/(TOTAL - 1)                      071
      RATIO = VAR/MEAN                                                 072
  170 FORMAT (10A8)                                                    073
  171 FORMAT (I2,F4.0)                                                 074
  172 FORMAT (1H1, 10A8)                                               075
  173 FORMAT (9H0 MEAN = ,F6.3,14H   VARIANCE = ,F6.3,11H   RATIO = ,  076
     1 F6.3)                                                           077
                                                                       078
                                                                       079
*****SELECT DISTRIBUTIONS TO BE FITTED*****                            080
                                                                       081
                                                                       082
  210 IF (MEAN - VAR) 305, 500, 500                                    083
                                                                       084
                                                                       085
      FITTING OF POISSON AND NEGATIVE-BINOMIAL DISTRIBUTIONS           086
                                                                       087
  305 PF = MEAN/VAR                                                    088
      WRITE (6,373)                                                    089
      WRITE (6,375)                                                    090
      Q = 1.- PF                                                       091
      AK = MEAN**2/(VAR-MEAN)                                          092
      B(1) = PF**AK                                                    093
      P(1) = EXP(-MEAN)                                                094
      CMP(1) = P(1)                                                    095
      CMB(1) = B(1)                                                    096
      REL(1) = FRQ(1)/TOTAL                                            097
      DELT(1) = FRQ(1)/TOTAL                                           098
      DO 350   I=2,IW                                                  099
      P(I) = MEAN*P(I-1)/(I-1)                                         100
      B(I) = B(I-1)*Q*(I+AK-2)/(I-1)                                   101
      DELT(I) = FRQ(I)/TOTAL                                           102
      REL(I) = REL(I-1) + FRQ(I)/TOTAL                                 103
      CMP(I) = CMP(I-1) + P(I)                                         104
  350 CMB(I) = CMB(I-1) + B(I)                                         105
      DO 360   I=1,IW                                                  106
      THP(I) = P(I)*TOTAL                                              107
      THB(I) = B(I)*TOTAL                                              108
      X = I-1                                                          109
  360 WRITE (6, 380) X, FRQ(I),DELT(I), THP(I), P(I), THB(I), B(I)     110
      WRITE (6,173)   MEAN, VAR, RATIO                                 111
      WRITE (6, 371)                                                   112
  370 FORMAT (2X,I2,F10.0,4F10.3,6X,F6.1,3F10.3,6X,F6.1)               113
  371 FORMAT (* SINCE THE RATIO OF THE VARIANCE TO THE MEAN IS GREATER 114
```

```
     1THAN UNITY, THE POISSON AND NEGATIVE-BINOMIAL DISTRIBUTIONS HAVE
     2BEEN FITTED.*)
 373 FORMAT (6H0EVENT,3X,14H OBSERVED DATA,5X,5X,21H POISSON DISTRIBUTI
     1ON, 8X,31H NEGATIVE-BINOMIAL DISTRIBUTION)
 375 FORMAT (*               FRQ       PROB               FRQ       PROB
     1         FRQ       PROB*)
 380 FORMAT (2X, I2, F10.0, F10.3, 9X, 2F10.3, 10X, 2F10.3)
     GO TO 1500
C
C   *****FIT GENERALIZED--POISSON DISTRIBUTION*****
C
C
 500 WRITE (6, 580)
     DO 501    I = 1, IW
     N = XL
     X = I-1
 501 WRITE (6, 582) X, FRQ(I)
 505 DO 555  K=1, 5
     PARAM = K*MEAN + (K-1)/2
     WRITE (6,570) K, PARAM, MEAN
     T(1) = EXP(-PARAM)
     NUM = (N+1)*K
     DO 510 J=2, NUM
 510 T(J) = PARAM*T(J-1)/(J-1)
     DO 530 IX=1, N
     L = K*IX + 1
     M = K*(IX + 1)
     SUM = 0
     DO 520  I = L, M
 520 SUM = SUM + T(I)
     THF = SUM*TOTAL
 530 WRITE (6,571)  IX, SUM, THF
 555 CONTINUE
 570 FORMAT (41H0FITTED GENERALIZED--POISSON DISTRIBUTION/
     1        22H WITH PARAMETER  K = ,I2/
     2        27H        PARAMETER LAMBDA = ,F6.3/
     3        15H       MEAN = ,F6.3//
     4        36H EVENT    PROBABILITY    THEORETICAL/
     5                   24X,10H FREQUENCY)
 571 FORMAT (4H  ,I2,8X,F5.3,10X,F6.1)
 580 FORMAT (19H0 EVENT  FREQUENCY)
 582 FORMAT (2X, I2, F15.0)
1500 CONTINUE
1600 GO TO 10
1700 CONTINUE
     END
```

APPENDIX K

CHI-SQUARE TEST OF FITTING OF SCHUHL DISTRIBUTION

For readers interested in the goodness of fit of the time-spacing distribution represented by the formula here developed, the following chi-square (χ^2) test data are submitted.

The author has found it desirable to replace the value of the various parameters given in the text by the following values:

$$t_1 = 1.98 \qquad t_2 = 13.16 \qquad \gamma = 0.583$$
$$\varepsilon = 0.81 \qquad\qquad\qquad 1 - \gamma = 0.417$$

These lead to the formula

$$0.583e^{-\frac{(\theta - 0.81)}{1.17}} + 0.417e^{-\frac{\theta}{13.16}}$$

in percent of the total number of spacings (Fig. 6) and

$$385 \times 10^{-0.37\,(\theta - 0.81)} + 275 \times 10^{-0.033\theta}$$

in number of spacings (table).

Col. 1 gives the limits of the intervals in which the spacings are classed.

Col. 2 the theoretical number of spacings n, corresponding to the entries in Column 1.

Col. 3 the theoretical number of spacings f_t comprised between times given by Column 1.

Col. 4 the observed number of f_o corresponding to f_t of Column 3.

Col. 5 the deviation $f_t - f_o$.

Col. 6 the values of $\dfrac{(f_t - f_o)^2}{f_t}$. The sum of this column, namely

$$\sum \frac{(f_t - f_o)^2}{f_t}, \text{ is } \chi^2.$$

127

FITTING OF THE LAW

$$n = 385 \times 10^{-0.37(\theta-0.81)} + 275 \times 10^{-0.033\theta}$$

(Chi-Square Test)

θ	n	f_t	f_o	$f_t - f_o$	$\dfrac{(f_t - f_o)^2}{f_t}$
0	660				
1	582.34	77.66	78	−0.34	0.00
2	375.92	206.42	207	−0.58	0.00
3	278.53	97.39	94	+3.39	0.12
4	228.34	50.19	58	−7.81	1.22
5	198.91	29.43	24	+5.43	1.00
6	178.94	19.97	17	+2.97	0.44
7	163.53	15.41	23	−7.59	3.74
8	150.58	12.95	11	+1.95	0.29
10	128.78	21.80	18	+3.80	0.66
12	110.52	18.26	23	−4.74	1.23
14	94.91	15.61	20	−4.39	1.23
16	81.53	13.38	16	−2.62	0.51
18	70.04	11.49	7	+4.49	1.75
20	60.16	9.88	6	+3.88	1.52
22	51.68	8.48	4	+4.48	2.37
24	44.40	7.28	6	+1.28	0.22
26	38.13	6.27	6	+0.27	0.01
31	26.08	12.05	10	+2.05	0.35
36	17.84	8.24	11	−2.76	0.92
41	12.20	5.64	8	−2.36	0.99
46	8.34	3.86	6	−2.14	1.19
51	5.71	2.63	1	+1.63	1.01
61	2.67	3.04	4	−0.96	0.30
71	1.25	1.42	1	+0.42	0.12
00	0.00	1.25	1	+0.25	0.05

chi-square = 21.24

Degrees of Freedom = 25 − 5 = 20

APPENDIX L

Since André Schuhl proposed a composite Poisson-type distribution to describe vehicle headways in 1955, other researchers have investigated means of applying his work to actual empirical data. In 1962 Kell utilized a modified version of the Schuhl headway distribution in the development of a simulation model (1). In 1968, Grecco and Sword published a study of fitting of headway data from US52 Bypass near Lafayette, Indiana (2). They used the following form of the Schuhl equation:

$$P(h \geqslant x) = \gamma e^{-\frac{x-\epsilon}{t_1}} + (1 - \gamma) e^{-\frac{x}{t_2}} \tag{1}$$

where $P(h \geqslant x) =$ probability of a headway greater than or equal to time x

$\gamma =$ fraction of vehicles in the retarded group
$\epsilon =$ minimum headway of vehicles in the retarded group
$t_1 =$ average headway of vehicles in the retarded group
$t_2 =$ average headway of vehicles in the free-moving group
$x =$ time
$e =$ base of Napierian (natural) logarithms.

The use of this equation requires a determination of the parameters γ, t_1, and t_2. Grecco and Sword found the following estimating relationships:

$$\gamma = .00115V \tag{2}$$

$$t_1 = 2.5 \tag{3}$$

$$t_2 = 24 - .0122V \tag{4}$$

where V = lane volume

Their findings were that these estimating relationships resulted in a statistically acceptable fit of the Schuhl headway

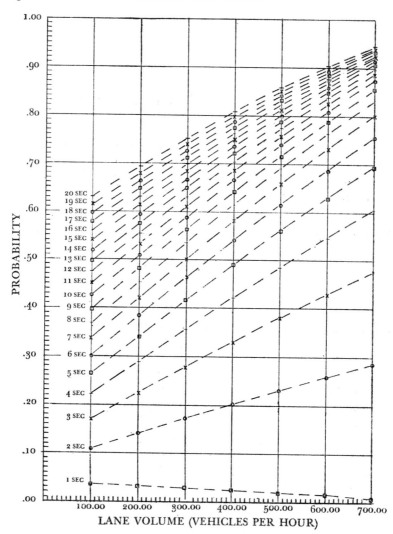

FIGURE L-1.   Probability of a headway less than x seconds.
Source: Grecco, W. L., and Sword, E. C., "Prediction of Parameters for Schuhl's Headway Distribution," *Traffic Engineering*, Vol. 38, No. 5, February 1968, pp. 36-38.

distribution as shown in equation 1 for lane volumes up to 700 vehicles per hour. The form of equation 1 that results from the substitution of the relationships is:

$$P(h \geq x) = \frac{115\,Ve^{-\frac{x-1}{2.5}}}{100,000} + \left(1 - \frac{115V}{100,000}\right) e^{-\frac{x}{24-.0122V}} \quad (5)$$

$$x \geq 1.0 \text{ sec.}$$

This study also developed a nomograph for determining the probability of a headway less than x seconds. It is shown in Figure L-1.

It should be emphasized that these estimating relationships were developed using data from one particular location. There is no guarantee that the figures shown are applicable to all roads. However, the methods used in the development of these values should be valid for use anywhere.

REFERENCES FOR APPENDIX L

1. Kell, James H., "Analyzing Vehicular Delay at Intersections Through Simulation," *Highway Research Board Bulletin 356*, 1962, pp. 28–39.
2. Grecco, W. L., and Sword, E. C., "Prediction of Parameters for Schuhl's Headway Distribution," *Traffic Engineering*, Vol. 38, No. 5, February 1968, pp. 36–38.

APPENDIX M

It is interesting to show how to calculate X_m from the formula

$$X_m = \int_0^{\theta_2} \frac{j(y)}{j(\theta_2)} E(2\theta_2 - y)\, dy \qquad (1)$$

when $\theta_2 > \theta_1$. The calculations are shown below without the complete derivations.

1. The function $f(x)$ is always equal to N when $X < \theta_1$, but it is not possible to define the function, when $\theta_1 \leqslant x < \theta_2$, otherwise than in line 2 of the 3 equations grouped as (17) in the text. This equation, moreover, permits the calculation of $f(x)$ and its successive derivatives for $x = \theta_1$ and as a consequence, under certain restrictions regarding the function $f(x)$, to define it by a Taylor series expansion of $x = \theta_1$. We find that:

$$f(\theta_1) \quad = N - j(\theta_1)$$
$$f'(\theta_1) \quad = f(\theta_1)\, p(o) - N\, p(o) + N\, p(\theta_1)$$
$$f''(\theta_1) \quad = f'(\theta_1)\, p(o) + f(\theta_1)\, p'(o) - N\, p'(o) + N\, p'(\theta_1)$$

$$\qquad \vdots \qquad\qquad \vdots \qquad\qquad\qquad \vdots \qquad\qquad\qquad (2)$$

$$f^{(n)}(\theta_1) \quad = \sum_{k=1}^{n} f^{(n-k)}(\theta_1)\, p^{(k-1)}(o) - N p^{(n-1)}(o) + N p^{(n-1)}(\theta_1)$$

The exponents in parentheses (n) designating the derivative of the order n, and

$$f(x) = f(\theta_1 + u) = f(\theta_1) + \frac{u}{1} f'(\theta_1)$$

$$+ \frac{u^2}{2} f''(\theta_1) + \ldots + \frac{u^n}{n!} f^{(n)}(\theta_1) + \ldots$$

when

$$\theta_1 \leqslant x < \theta_2 \quad \text{or} \quad 0 \leqslant u < (\theta_2 - \theta_1)$$

2. The function $E(x)$ is equal to unity when $x < \theta_1$, and takes the value $1 - P(\theta_1)$ when $\theta_1 \leqslant x < \theta_2$. When $\theta_2 < x < 2\theta_2$, $E(x)$ can be calculated by virtue of the relation

$$\frac{\partial E(x)}{\partial x} = \frac{-j(\theta_2)}{N} f(x - \theta_2),$$

which gives when

$$\theta_2 \leqslant x < (\theta_2 + \theta_1) \quad \text{or} \quad 0 \leqslant v < \theta_1 \quad \text{if} \quad v = x - \theta_2$$

$$E(x) = E(\theta_2 + v) = 1 - P(\theta_1) - v\, j(\theta_2) \tag{3}$$

When

$$(\theta_2 + \theta_1) < x < 2\theta_2 \quad \text{or} \quad 0 < w < (\theta_2 - \theta_1) \quad \text{if} \quad w = x - \theta_2 - \theta_1$$

$$E(x) = E(\theta_2 + \theta_1 + w)$$

$$= 1 - P(\theta_1) - \theta_1\, j(\theta_2) - \frac{j(\theta_2)}{N} \int_0^w f(\theta_1 + w)\, dw \tag{4}$$

3. One can then separate the range of application of equation (1) into two parts:

one, $\theta_2 \leqslant (2\theta_2 - y) < (\theta_2 + \theta_1)$ in which $E(2\theta_2 - y)$ is represented by expression (3) above where $v = \theta_2 - y$

the other, $(\theta_2 + \theta_1) \leqslant (2\theta_2 - y) < 2\theta_2$ in which $E(2\theta_2 - y)$ is represented by expression (4) above where $w = \theta_2 - \theta_1 - y$

Then

$$X_m = \int_{\theta_2 - \theta_1}^{\theta_2} \frac{j(y)}{j(\theta_2)} [1 - P(\theta_1) - j(\theta_2)(\theta_2 - y)]\, dy$$

$$+ \int_0^{\theta_2 - \theta_1} \frac{j(y)}{j(\theta_2)} [1 - P(\theta_1) - j(\theta_2)\, \theta_1]\, dy$$

$$- \int_0^{\theta_2 - \theta_1} \frac{j(y)}{N}\, dy \int_0^{\theta_2 - \theta_1 - y} f(\theta_1 + w)\, dw$$

The first two terms are calculated without difficulty and yield:

$$\frac{[1 - P(\theta_1)]\,[1 - P(\theta_2)]}{j(\theta_2)} - \theta_1 + \int_{\theta_2-\theta_1}^{\theta_2} P(x)\,dx \qquad (5)$$

To calculate the last term we note that

$$-\frac{j(y)}{N} = -1 + \frac{y}{1}\,p(o) + \frac{y^2}{2}\,p'(o) + \ldots + \frac{y^n}{n!}\,p^{(n-1)}\,(o) + \ldots$$

$$\int_0^{\theta_2-\theta_1-y} f(\theta_1 + w)\,dw = \frac{(\theta_2 - \theta_1 - y)}{1}\,f(\theta_1)$$

$$+ \frac{(\theta_2 - \theta_1 - y)^2}{2}\,f'(\theta_1) + \ldots + \frac{(\theta_2 - \theta_1 - y)^p}{p!}\,f^{(p-1)}\,(\theta_1) + \ldots$$

These calculations can then be made and taking account of the relationships of (2) one obtains the sum of two series

$$-\frac{(\theta_2 - \theta_1)^2}{2}\,N + \frac{(\theta_2 - \theta_1)^3}{3!}\,p(o) + \frac{(\theta_2 - \theta_1)^4}{4!}\,p'(o) + \ldots$$

$$+ \frac{(\theta_2 - \theta_1)^2}{2}\,j(\theta_1) - \frac{(\theta_2 - \theta_1)^3}{3!}\,p(\theta_1) - \frac{(\theta_2 - \theta_1)^4}{4!}\,p'(\theta_1) + \ldots$$

in which we recognize the Taylor series

$$-R(\theta_2 - \theta_1) + R(o) - \frac{(\theta_2 - \theta_1)}{1}\,P(o)$$

$$+R(\theta_2) - R(\theta_1) + \frac{(\theta_2 - \theta_1)}{1}\,P(\theta_1)$$

where

$$R(x) = \int_x^\infty P(x)\,dx$$

We can then write the last term of X_m

$$-\int_{\theta_2-\theta_1}^{\theta_2} P(x)\,dx + \int_0^{\theta_1} P(x)\,dx - \theta_2 + \theta_1 + (\theta_2 - \theta_1)\,P(\theta_1)$$

and on adding this to the expression above (5) for the first two terms of X_m, we find that

$$X_m = \frac{[1 - P(\theta_1)]\,[1 - P(\theta_2)]}{j(\theta_2)} - \theta_2 + (\theta_2 - \theta_1)\,P(\theta_1) + \int_0^{\theta_1} P(x)\,dx$$